The Engineer and Construction Control

W. L. Elsby

Thomas Telford Limited
1981

Thomas Telford Ltd, Telford House, 26–34 Old Street, London EC1
© W. L. Elsby. 1981
ISBN 0 7277 0117 7

Set in 11/12 pt Ehrhardt and printed in Great Britain by Henry Ling Ltd, at the Dorset Press, Dorchester, Dorset

Introduction

The engineer's principal object in contract supervision should broadly be to supervise construction in accordance with the contract terms, with the aim of maximizing the rate of return to the promoter on his investment in the project as a whole. During construction, the engineer often has to choose one of several technically feasible courses of action, none conflicting with the contract, in which case he should aim at choosing that satisfying this criterion. The engineer should also recognize the contractor's need to make a profit and should assist him to do so provided that such action is within the contract terms, and is not taken at the expense of the promoter.

The engineer has responsibilities in assuring safety, quality, construction progress and financial control, all of which require action taken at appropriate times. There is little consolation in reviewing structural risk after failure has occurred, bearing losses in returns when completion is late, receiving advice of large cost increases at the end of the contract, or enduring any other of construction's misfortunes. The engineer is in a powerful position to prevent such evils and to assist the contractor in controlling his costs. It is hoped that what is provided here in the way of a control system and its operation will be of use to engineers in doing so.

Special consideration has been given to the physical problems of construction, not at the expense of other aspects of supervision but because they are often intractable. It is frequently said that, beyond measuring work done, contesting claims, reviewing progress and programme, and urging the contractor on to greater efforts, the engineer has little power or responsibility for controlling construction costs and delays in completion. This is not so. He can alter designs and take other action to avoid circumstances which would lead to valid claims. He can to a large extent control the ordering of unjustified alterations. And, most important, he can investigate and analyse construction problems and negotiate treatments of them with the contractor. Most contracts provide the engineer with powers of demand or direction of the contractor to take appropriate action, and the 'ICE Conditions of Contract' (Fifth Edition) (ref. 7) are unequivocal in this respect. Such powers should be used only in the last resort, and, moreover, only after the engineer has investigated and analysed the problem and attempted to negotiate a solution with the contractor; otherwise he will have neither given the contractor the opportunity of preparing fully considered proposals nor prepared them himself. Promoters often have to bear enormous cost increases and postponements of project returns as a result of these problems; the need for methods of dealing with them is evidently a pressing unfulfilled aim of supervision.

There is a world of difference between working a control system to rule and using it to solve difficult problems. Fortunately there exist such qualities as ingenuity, judgement and tenacity, the nature and effects of which words do not easily describe. In this respect the main text and the Appendix enlarge on the operations of a control system and recommend policies the engineer should adopt in implementing it, that is in the practice of supervision.

The engineer's position in relation to national and sector economic conditions, and the promoter's identification and evaluation of a project are examined in Chapter 6. A short review of national and sector studies, and of project feasibility studies and appraisals, has been given. The review indicates the value of including design and construction engineers in economic studies preceding the decision to carry out a project, and the benefits to governments, industry and the engineering profession of doing so.

The terms *economy* and *economic* have been used in relation to costs and benefits. The former indicates commercial costs and benefits and the latter, costs and benefits to the national economy. The engineer will recognize the relevance of commercial figures, as in the Appendix examples, and economists will in practice estimate economic figures, as in the Chapter 6 feasibility studies of public projects, often from estimates in commercial figures prepared by the engineer.

CONTENTS

1. A control system

A system for supervising civil engineering construction from the time work starts on site is described here. Construction carried out under contract is discussed but, with minimal and obvious minor amendments, the text applies equally to work carried out directly by a promoter, as direct work does not affect the need for an engineering function nor a contracting function.

The work to be accomplished and conditions governing its accomplishment may be laid down in an agreement, general conditions of contract, contract drawings, specifications, bill of quantities, tender, outline construction programme and description of construction methods. This contract document is supplemented as the work proceeds by the contractor's detailed programmes, temporary works details, detailed descriptions of construction methods and the like, prepared by the contractor and approved by the engineer, and by instructions, agreements, and additional drawings, specifications and bills of quantities issued by the engineer. The result is a set of documents essential to the carrying out of the work.

The documents provide the whole basis for supervision but do not, and are not intended to, provide the engineer with an adequate system for managing supervision. They do not, for instance, ensure that the engineer foresees the need for alterations to avoid future delay; that the promoter is continually advised of the best practicable estimate of the final total cost so he can reconsider his financing, adjust his overall budgets, curtail the project and so on; that necessary inspections and tests are always carried out; nor that every practicable assistance is given to the contractor. The engineer needs some form of terse day-to-day construction control system which enables him to foresee and clearly identify any, and preferably all, problems which may affect the construction process.

1

The engineer's function is to assist in construction as required by the contract, and this will include attention to

(*a*) safety of the permanent and temporary works
(*b*) safety of personnel
(*c*) quality of materials and workmanship
(*d*) construction progress
(*e*) financial control

This does not prevent him from helping the contractor in every practicable way, provided that the promoter's legitimate interests are not adversely affected.

Certain external factors affect a project. First, the achievement of the objectives will not necessarily assure the achievement of a worthwhile project. The best of economic and political studies leading to a decision to carry out a project is always to an appreciable degree unreliable and particularly so in forecasting its long-term effects. The uncertainty is inseparable from projects and not something the engineer can dispel. It is, however, important that the engineer, having accepted an assignment, does not allow the uncertainty to breed loss of commitment. Small losses of commitment cause large losses of efficiency. Second, execution of a project is affected, sometimes considerably, by relations between labour and management. No advice on such questions is offered, except that the system can and should be pursued however difficult labour and management relations may become.

A specimen construction control system is presented in Chapter 2. It is presented at this stage to enable the reader to get an early picture of the document central to control as it is seen here. Most of the specimen system will be self-explanatory, and, where it is not, later chapters offer enlargement and explanation.

The specimen control system is an example of a system which has been used with minor adaptations in eight different countries over a period of 20 years. The example used is for a major harbour contract. This form of presentation by example has been used for two reasons: first, any general manual on construction supervision, applicable to all forms of construction, would be either so confined to general principles as to

2

be vague, or so lengthy as to bury essentials under detail; and second, the specimen method of presentation, while avoiding these pitfalls, provides a document which experienced engineers would have no difficulty in modifying to suit various types of construction and forms of contract. The preparation of any control system should, however, be checked by a contract expert to ensure that it conforms with the terms of the particular form of contract to be used, especially if it is an overseas contract under, or affected by, foreign law.

In general, neither in the specimen control system nor elsewhere within these pages is the distinction made between the engineer ultimately responsible under the contract (e.g. consulting engineer or promoter's chief engineer) and his representative on site (the engineer's representative or resident engineer). The reasons are that the powers and responsibilities of the engineer ultimately responsible and those of the engineer's representative or resident engineer may differ according to the conditions of contract in use and the policy of the engineer ultimately responsible. For study purposes, the reader may interpret the word *engineer* in its context according to the practice of his firm or department. In practice, the engineer ultimately responsible will define the distinction, and it should be noted that Note 1 on page 5, at the start of the specimen system, makes provision for this. Once this has been done, the person or persons on the head office and site staffs directly responsible for each function can be designated. If, as is usual, the staff is not complex, the designation can be indicated by title (not by name) against the appropriate paragraphs of the system.

The specimen control system (SCS) is presented in short statements (numbered paragraphs) as this is all that experienced engineers, or younger engineers having access to experienced engineers, will need. For the same reason, the system does not indicate further action needed, where such action would be obvious to an experienced engineer.

As the specimen system relates to an actual harbour contract, it includes provisions particular to that contract: a breakwater warning system (SCS§4), certain measures required by the Harbour Master (SCS§6), and particular attention to safety tests for certain bridge steelwork (SCS§14). This raises the question as to how much special provision should be made in a control system. The answer is only for such action as is not adequately provided for by the master copy of the contract details, programmes and schedules specified in the control system, the financial review, minutes of meetings, inspection and correspondence. Otherwise, control systems become continuously more unwieldly over the years. It may be noted that all special provisions of the specimen system refer to questions of safety.

2. Specimen control system for a major harbour contract

NOTES

1 A Partner will define the interpretations of the term *engineer* by letter. Members of head office staff and site staff directly responsible for each function will then be designated by title.
2 *Alteration* includes *addition*.

CONTENTS

SECTION I
MASTER COPY OF CONTRACT DETAILS

1 Maintain securely in the engineer's representative's office

(*a*) a copy set of the original contract drawings
(*b*) notes on drawings referring to Variation Orders, Provisional and P.C. Sum Orders, Provisional Item Orders, working drawings (see (*h*)) and relevant letters (see (*k*))

5

(*c*) drawings of Variations, Provisional and P.C. Sum works

(*d*) notes on relevant drawings referring to makers' drawings and makers' installation and operating instructions

(*e*) makers' drawings and makers' installation instructions

(*f*) survey and setting-out drawings noted to date

(*g*) temporary works drawings noted to date

(*h*) working drawings (ie. drawings detailing work shown on the original contract drawings but considered by the engineer not to include any Variation) noted to date

(*i*) contract conditions, specifications and bills of quantities, with notes referring to Variation Orders, Provisional and P.C. Sum Orders and letters referred to in (*k*)

(*j*) files of orders, specifications and bills of quantities for Variations, Provisional Sum and P.C. Sum items and Provisional items

(*k*) a file of letters issued by the engineer, and any associated drawings, specifications, bills of quantities and any other relevant documents

   (*i*) recording any agreement with the contractor enabling him to deviate from the master copy of the contract details, on condition that it entails no additional cost to the promoter or that it offers a reduction in his costs

   (*ii*) ordering or approving measures for which the engineer, in disagreement with the contractor, considers no payment due

   (*iii*) providing a method of payment where the engineer considers payment justified by the contract but for which the specified measurement provides no method

   (*iv*) informing the contractor of the engineer's approval or rejection of proposals made by the contractor for expediting progress when the engineer considers the rate of progress too slow and the reason for the slow progress does not entitle the contractor to an extension of time;

and advising the contractor that he will not be entitled to additional payment for implementing approved proposals

2 Arrange for the site engineer (drawing office) to keep the master copy of the contract details, and for the quantity surveyor to keep copies of the annotated contract conditions, specifications and bill of quantities; files of orders, specifications and bills of quantities for Variations, Provisional Sum and P.C. Sum items and Provisional items; and files of letters, specifications, bills of quantities and similar documents relevant to the letters referred to in §1(*k*).

3 Establish a routine ensuring that the head office and site office inform each other of any alteration they make to the master copy of the contract details. Establish also a routine ensuring that the site engineer (drawing office) and, as appropriate, the quantity surveyor are informed of all alterations (e.g. instructions to authorized signatories).

SECTION II
SAFETY OF PERSONNEL AND PERMANENT AND TEMPORARY WORKS

4 Arrange warning systems and drill to prevent injury to men working on the breakwaters in the event of a wave over-topping the breakwater.

5 Review the contractor's arrangements for providing for the safety of personnel, complying with statutory requirements and any additional needs. Programme and carry out inspections. Report results to the contractor and, if his reaction is unsatisfactory, the promoter.

6 Check contractor's temporary works designs to the extent necessary to avoid failure. Obtain in writing Harbour Master's approval of breakwaters and lock construction methods, including navigation lighting.

7 Permit no deviations from the permanent works details shown in the master copy of the contract details (§§101, 103). Review deviations to temporary works and act accordingly.

8 Prepare and carry out programmes for periodically

checking the line and level of permanent and temporary works, and existing works (including slopes) which might be affected. Restrict the procedure to critical points.

9   Prepare and carry out programmes for periodically checking soundings alongside permanent structures and in the harbour entrance and channel for scour or accretion. Before detailed sounding, spot-sound to check the need for it.

10   Prepare and carry out programmes for periodically checking wave action at selected points within the harbour and compare the results with wave model forecasts.

11   Test-load bearing piles, establish criteria for estimating safe loads during driving and apply to every pile. Record results. Repeat test-loadings as necessary.

12   Obtain soil samples occasionally at random and also where soils excavated or dredged appear different from those assumed in design. Test the samples and check design calculations.

13   Inspect, test and record approval of all work to be covered, including

(*a*)   foundations under and above water
(*b*)   drains
(*c*)   holding-down bolts
(*d*)   tie-bars and wrappings
(*e*)   water pipes

14   Review the results of inspection and testing on or off site (§§92–103) which have a special bearing on the safety of permanent works, with particular reference to inspections and tests of welding, safety devices on equipment, and the existing steelwork of the western road approach bridges. Supplement them if necessary.

15   Up-date inspections and tests with special bearing on safety of works, as additional works are ordered.

16   Maintain a frequent review of these measures; maintain vigilance in site inspections and discussions with engineer's design and site staff and with contractor's staff, with the object of recognizing signs of present dangers and foreseeing future dangers, with particular attention to soil and hydraulic conditions.

17 Report at reasonable intervals on effectiveness and economy in staff; a short report, mainly on exceptions.

SECTION III
PROVISIONAL AND P.C. SUMS

18 Programme the preparation of Provisional Sum and P.C. Sum works contract details to phase with the contract programme (§28). Allow generous time for preparation of documents, agreeing selection of tenderers, tendering, selection of any sub-contractor and construction.

19 Estimate the construction costs (including costs of any delay), reprogramme the work if necessary and practicable and assess any delay in the completion of the works due to each Provisional Sum work or P.C. Sum work when sufficient information on the work has been obtained.

20 If the estimated cost (including costs of any delay) or the assessed delay in completion of the works appears excessive, treat the item as an alteration (§§43–54 as appropriate).

21 Follow the procedures required by the conditions of contract and indicated in the main bills of quantities to prepare contract details for P.C. Sum items. Prepare contract details (drawings, specification, bill of quantities) for Provisional Sum items in the normal way.

22 Issue the order to the contractor as a numbered Provisional Sum or P.C. Sum Order, as appropriate, related to the relevant item or items of the main bills of quantities (§49).

23 Enter the consequences in the control system (§50).

24 Follow procedures stipulated in the conditions of contract for ordering, supervising and making payment for work carried out by a subcontractor nominated by the engineer.

SECTION IV
ALTERATIONS AND DELAYS

Normal supervision
Minor alterations
25 Identify any expected alteration as being a minor alteration; that is, not within the categories described in §39.

26 Adopt §§43–50 or 51–54 as applicable, simplifying them to suit the minor nature of the alteration.

Programme

27 Soon after starting work on site, examine the contractor's network construction programme, temporary works drawings, drawings showing main stages, details of equipment, and construction methods. Arrange with the contractor, as may be necessary, for indication on the programme of ordering and delivery of temporary works materials, temporary works construction, ordering and delivery of construction equipment, erection of equipment, ordering and delivery of materials and equipment for permanent works, construction of permanent works not shown on the original programme, an indication of the expected critical path, anticipated labour needs (classified by trade), and the value of permanent work to be done at various stages.

28 Discuss with the contractor a programme for carrying out work scheduled under Provisional and P.C. Sum items and for the preparation of contract details by the engineer. Arrange for these to be added to the contract programme.

29 Discuss the complement and experience of the contractor's 'key' men (subagents, general foremen, senior engineers and foremen), and the methods of construction and expected productivities of construction equipment, with the contractor. Wherever practicable, inspect construction equipment before delivery to the site and arrange with the contractor for any deficiencies to be remedied. Allow him the benefit of any doubts, but advise him in writing of doubts.

30 Discuss with the contractor a programme for the preparation of Variation contract details and associated construction work, and for the supply of working drawings. Arrange with the contractor for these to be added to the contract programme.

31 Ensure that the contract programme correlates with interdependent projects and any action to be taken by the promoter (e.g. arranging way-leaves). Enter them and their salient dates on the contract programme.

Progress

32 Establish and maintain close relations with senior members of the contractor's site organization directly controlling construction with the objects of maintaining good communications, general reciprocal assistance, identifying problems causing or likely to cause delay and, as may be practicable, assisting in solving them by discussion.

33 Establish reasonable interpretations of standards of workmanship where specifications are not quantitative.

34 Give the contractor every assistance practicable consistent with the spirit of the contract, making particular efforts to see his problems as he sees them.

35 Keep to the dates for taking action required of the engineer to implement the contract programme.

36 Compare progress made against the contract programme and note shortfalls.

37 Do not press for the application of measures to eliminate shortfalls as soon as they occur but discuss them with the contractor, attempt to assist in formulating solutions without taking exceptional measures, and prepare for later action which may be needed if solutions have not been reached after a reasonable time.

38 Review the programme for future work with the contractor, initiate action to avoid foreseeable delays and consider the feasibility of altering the programme.

Problems (Chapter 3)
Problems list and review

39 Maintain a list of occasions for delay or alteration which have proved or might prove too difficult or too costly in their effects for normal supervision to control.

40 Select problems for consideration in the chronological order needed to avoid interference with the programme.

41 Consider whether some extra effort of supervision can resolve the difficulty. If so, implement it and delete the problem from the list. Delete also obviously unnecessary problems, such as clearly unjustified proposals for alterations.

42 Establish a close relationship with the promoter's representative to keep the promoter informed of problems, the

efforts being made to resolve them and likely effects on the final contract price and the completion date; and, as may be necessary, to expedite action required of him.

Alterations contemplated by the promoter to improve the project

43   If the problem appears to be soluble by a design alteration, prepare: outline drawings and/or descriptions of the proposed alteration; a preliminary estimate of construction costs, including costs of any delay for which the promoter would be liable; and an assessment of delay in the contract completion.

44   Discuss the proposed alteration and alternatives with the promoter and subsequently with both the promoter and the contractor, with the object of minimizing the number of alternatives to be further considered. If the contractor might be liable for any of the costs or delays due to the alteration, try to conduct discussions with him on the basis of 'what appears to be best for the project irrespective of liability'. Place on record with the contractor evidence of efforts to minimize the cost of his liability.

45   If it becomes evident during the consideration of the remaining options that they contain or entail substantial measures other than alterations to the works, treat the problems as described under 'Other construction problems' (§§68–81).

46   If the options do not contain nor entail substantial measures other than alterations to the works, discuss with the promoter whether the likely effects justify a more detailed economy evaluation (Chapter 4 and Appendix).

47   Obtain in writing the promoter's final selection of the proposed alteration to be implemented.

48   Prepare contract details (drawings, specifications, bill of quantities) for the selected alteration.

49   Select from §1 (*j*) and (*k*) the types of Order, agreement, approval or provision needed to implement all work to be done and payment to be made. If action appropriate to more than one of the categories Variation, Provisional Sum, P.C. Sum and Provisional Item is involved, choose one and issue a numbered Order (Variation, Provisional Sum, P.C. Sum or

Provisional Item) accordingly, including in it all necessary Orders and all agreements, approvals and provisions of the types described in §1 (*k*). Include provision for all work to be done and all payment to be made in one transmittal: do not attempt to distinguish between Variation, Provisional Sum, P.C. Sum and Provisional item in the transmittal, excepting as may be essential or convenient. If time permits, invite the contractor's prices for items for which the engineer is sure the promoter will be liable, negotiate and issue the Order for the work, or, if not, issue the Order, and obtain prices and negotiate later. If the work can be covered by a letter of agreement, approval and/or provision alone (§1 (*k*)), issue it.

50   Enter the Order or letter, drawings, specifications, bill of quantities and any other associated documents in the master copy of the contract details (§1), the timing of the work in the contract programme (§§27–31), any effect on the estimated final contract price in the financial review (Section VII), any necessary programmed or scheduled action in the appropriate programmes and schedules (§133), any residual claim or expected residual claim in the claims register and claims list respectively (§§116, 117), and any residual problem in the problems list (§39).

Alterations contemplated by the engineer

51   Where alteration is considered essential for technical reasons (e.g. structural safety), follow §§43–50. Discuss the procedure with the promoter to keep him informed without too close an involvement.

52   Where alteration may be advisable for technical reasons but not essential (e.g. to simplify construction), follow the procedure of §§43–50.

53   Where alteration may be advisable to improve the project technically (e.g. to adopt a more modern type of construction than that originally proposed), follow the procedure of §§43–50.

54   Modify the detail with which alterations are treated by the procedures set out in §§51–53, according to the impact the engineer judges the alteration would have on the project. Tighten the procedure if small alterations tend to proliferate or

if a proposed alteration is not clearly based on benefits to the project economy or on necessity.

Alterations proposed by the contractor

55 If the contractor proposes a small and reasonable alteration to design, to reduce his time and/or costs of construction, implement it by the method set out in §49 except when §1 (*k* (*ii*)) applies. Issue a letter of the type in §1 (*k*(*ii*)) approving the alteration only if the probable benefit to the promoter justifies the risk of his being proved liable. If the proposal is not accepted, retain any residual problem on the problems list for further consideration.

56 Enter any consequences in the control system (§50).

57 If the design alteration proposed is considerable, obtain from the contractor the following: outline drawings clearly illustrating the proposed alteration and showing how it would fit in with the existing contract drawings; an outline specification for any new type of work; an itemized estimate of construction costs, including costs of any delay; an assessment of any delay in, or advancement of, the contract completion date; an outline of the contract programme, showing any changes.

58 Inform the contractor at the outset of the proposal that a priced bill of quantities similar to the contract bills will be needed from him before a final evaluation of his proposal can be made.

59 Discuss the proposal with the contractor with the object of agreeing any amendments to the outline drawings and specification needed to make the proposal acceptable to the promoter and the engineer, subject to the effect on the contract price and programme. If agreement cannot be reached, reject the alteration proposed, and, if necessary, retain the problem on the problems list for further treatment; if agreement is reached, ask the contractor to confirm or revise his estimate of cost and programme changes.

60 Review the contractor's estimate of cost and programme changes and discuss them with the contractor on a preliminary basis. Amend these as the engineer thinks fit, to obtain the engineer's estimate of cost and programme changes.

61 Estimate the final contract price including the proposed

alteration, by substituting the engineer's estimate of cost in the current financial review, quantifying and substituting any expected effects on all items of the review (§123).

62   Review the estimated final contract price and completion date both with and without the proposed alteration, and any estimated differences in annual maintenance costs after commissioning. If the estimated benefits to the promoter do not clearly outweigh any risk of increases in the contract price and increases in construction time, discuss with the promoter whether a more detailed economy evaluation of alternatives is needed. If so assist the promoter as required (Chapter 4 and Appendix).

63   If the proposed alteration is not considered justified, reject it, if necessary retaining the problem on the problems list for further treatment. If it appears to be justified, examine the contractor's priced bill of quantities in detail. Amend the bill descriptions, measurement definitions, approximate quantities etc. as needed and negotiate prices with the contractor. If the price presented by the resulting priced bill exceeds the engineer's estimate of cost (§§59, 60), review the effects on the operations described in §§61 and 62.

64   If at any time during the consideration of the proposed alteration it appears sufficiently likely to be justified, begin preparation of full drawings and specification or, if appropriate, ask the contractor to do so. If, after the review described in §63, the proposed alteration is acceptable, arrange for the preparation to be completed.

65   Keep the promoter informed.

66   Issue a numbered Variation Order, Provisional Sum Order or P.C. Sum Order as applicable and include any needed agreement, Order, approval or provision of the types described in §1 (*k*(*i*)–(*iv*)). Ensure that the Order informs the contractor of all measures the engineer considers to be the contractor's liability and of any intention the engineer has for further price negotiation.

67   Enter the consequences in the control system (§50).

Other construction problems

68   Construction problems selected from the problems list

may be recognized as not completely soluble by alterations to the permanent works alone. Such problems are considered in this section. It is also possible, though not likely, that, in examining alterations contemplated by the promoter or engineer or proposed by the contractor, feasible alternatives containing substantial measures other than alterations to the works may be recognized, in which case the whole problem should be reviewed as follows.

69 The problems will consist in general of effects of adverse labour relations, adverse physical conditions (including artificial obstructions), possible inadequacies of equipment or materials, or questions as to the suitability of management or labour.

70 If normal methods (§41) seem unlikely to resolve the problem, consider a simple programme for the following: method study of or operational research into the operations causing difficulty; additional site investigations; special tactics; services of technical or operations advisors; or trials of proposed treatments, as appropriate (Chapter 4 and Appendix).

71 If it is sufficiently likely that normal methods backed by the simple programme of §70 will be enough to overcome the difficulty, proceed with them as appropriate. Discuss treatments of the problem with the contractor and aim at that which will be optimal to both the promoter and the contractor within the terms of the contract.

72 Implement the treatment considered satisfactory and enter the consequences in the control system (§§49,50).

73 If the engineer considers that the simple programme (§70) would be inadequate or finds it so at some stage, discuss with the contractor more extensive measures which should be taken to identify feasible treatments. Agreement may be difficult to reach, particularly if the measures would be costly, such as extensive site investigation or a costly trial of a proposed treatment.

74 Record the history of the problem, delays attributable to it, the present position, efforts made to deal with the situation, and an outline description of any measures the engineer has suggested should be taken to identify possible

treatments. Present these to the contractor with a request for his comment and proposals.

75 If agreement on the measures needed is reached, implement them and enter the consequences in the control system (§§49,50). If agreement cannot be reached, review the proposals again and, in the last resort, decide whether the contractor's or the engineer's proposals should be implemented.

76 Issue an instruction or letter of agreement to the contractor, as appropriate, for the measures needed, taking care to avoid interference with the contractor's operations and responsibilities; enter the consequences in the control system (§§49,50).

77 As the results of the investigatory measures come forward, prepare preliminary details of feasible alternative treatments. They may include alterations to the works, changes in equipment or materials, rearrangement and perhaps strengthening of the engineer's or contractor's staff or of labour, changes in construction methods, or any combination of such remedies.

78 Discuss with the promoter whether an economy evaluation is needed to select the preferred treatment (Chapter 4 and Appendix). If it is needed, then assist the promoter as needed.

79 Select the preferred treatment in consultation with the promoter and the contractor.

80 Implement the treatment and enter the consequences in the control system (§§49,50).

81 Control the time taken to resolve the problem and staff man-hours engaged on it (§135).

SECTION V
WORKS SUPERVISION AND RECORDS

82 Discuss, in the normal course of supervision, inter-pretation of the control system and any possible deficiencies of the system, with staff members to whom direct responsibility has been allocated. Discuss cases where there appears to be no

room for compromise with the letter of the control system; cases where there is room for compromise and what will be reasonable compromise; methods of controlling the staff inputs; and opportunities for avoiding unnecessary work for the engineer and the contractor. Ensure that the more junior members of staff are given reasonable opportunity to read and discuss the system and their role in supervision.

Setting-out

83   Prepare as needed setting-out drawings for the whole site and setting-out drawings of special areas to a larger scale as needed. Take copies for use as 'as built' layout drawings.

84   Arrange with the contractor for main base lines to be marked by substantial concrete stations at the safest practicable locations, i.e. as clear as possible from future disturbance. Fix the locations of main stations by observations from permanent structures. Enter these on setting-out drawings and/or in field books as applicable.

85   Check bench-marks and setting-out stations at reasonable time intervals; check tide gauges often.

86   Set out

(*a*)   by targets, temporary base lines etc. which will be subject to the minimum of disturbance and as easy as practicable for site staff to use

(*b*)   giving attention to minimizing time spent on setting-out

87   Agree existing cross-sections with contractor's engineer and mutually sign level and sounding field books; obtain agreement of contractor's project manager and his signature to plotted cross-sections.

88   Number and store level, sounding and other field books.

Recorded information

89   Prepare 'as built' drawings and detailed progress drawings as work proceeds. Use one drawing for both purposes where practicable. Take progress photographs and photographs of any special situations or conditions.

90   Agree 'as excavated' foundation levels and slopes, and

basic details of other work to be covered, with the contractor's engineer and mutually sign agreed details. Instruct site staff that no other statement or information is to be added to these records.

91   Record disposal or reuse of recovered materials.

Inspection and testing

92   Carry out and check normal day-to-day inspection.

93   Schedule all special inspections and tests to be carried out off site or on site, excepting as provided for elsewhere in the system. Programme them where possible. Up-date the schedule and programmes as additional works are ordered.

94   Obtain necessary Standard Specifications.

95   Arrange with contractor the procedure for reviewing and approving proposed suppliers of materials or equipment for permanent works.

96   Check prices of materials and equipment included in any basic rates schedule.

97   Check that orders for materials or equipment comply with the contract.

98   Maintain a register of orders, including order number, date, supplier and identification of materials or equipment to be supplied, in sufficient detail to check adequacy of inspection and testing. Record date of inspection off site and on site, date of testing off site and on site, and reference to test certificates. Do not attempt to maintain more detailed information.

99   Check inspection and testing operations as necessary.

100   Arrange and check maintenance of site inspectors' daily diaries recording

(*a*)   input by item of labour and equipment employed on main items of work and in total on inspector's section
(*b*)   quantities of main items of work done and description of other work done on section
(*c*)   breakdowns and time lost due to each
(*d*)   weather conditions and time lost due to weather
(*e*)   other time lost, with causes
(*f*)   other difficulties or special events

101   Permit no deviations from the permanent works details shown in the master copy of the contract details.

102   Inspect site work thoroughly.

103   Instruct site staff not to stop construction work except as essential, and in this case to refer the circumstances to the engineer's representative or his deputy; also to refer any doubt as to standards of materials or workmanship to the engineer's representative or his deputy.

SECTION VI
PAYMENT

104   Make interim payments in accordance with the master copy of the contract details.

105   Check that the contractor's agent has informed his staff that no alterations to permanent works are to be undertaken except as ordered or agreed by him or staff nominated by him.

106   Examine and agree records of time-and-materials with the contractor only as authorized by the master copy of the contract details or, as may be reasonable, as requested by the contractor. Instruct site staff to agree records in the former case only, except as authorized by the engineer's representative, his deputy or the quantity surveyor, and to qualify the agreement as 'agreed without prejudice'.

107   Review efficiency of time-and-materials operations to minimize cost to the promoter.

108   Check methods of preparing and agreeing time-and-materials records as found necessary.

Interim measurement

109   Minimize time spent on interim measurement by adopting reasonable approximations. However, do not make approximations in ascertaining variations in cost due to escalation clauses, nor in ascertaining payments to be made on a time-and-materials basis.

110   Maintain permanent records of calculations of interim measurements, quoting sources of information such as level books and drawing numbers.

111   Make an accurate interim measurement once every four months to correct accrued errors. Estimate final quantities for inclusion in the periodic financial review of the contract price.

112   Arrange printing of measurement forms for Variation Orders, Provisional and P.C. Sum Orders etc.

Final measurement

113   Review interim measurements and bills of quantities to make final measurement as a particular item or a definable part of an item of work is completed.

114   Record, file securely and store details of final measurements including

(*a*)   the bill of quantities item number, the contract method of measurement and the rate

(*b*)   full calculations with references to all information used

115   Obtain contractor's signature to each final measurement, recording any reservation expressed by the contractor as a claim.

Claims

116   Enter each claim, numbered consecutively, in a claims register, using: short heading; short description of claim; references to correspondence; statement whether the contractor has quoted the condition of contract on which he has based the claim or if he has stated that it is for consideration *ex gratia*; the contractor's estimated cost; and the engineer's estimated cost to the promoter should payment be made.

117   Maintain a confidential list of claims which the engineer, as a result of conversation with the contractor or for other reasons, expects from the contractor.

118   Arrange for contractor to provide any drawings and/or written descriptions needed to define each claim. Agree records of time-and-materials 'without prejudice to the contract' and record any circumstances affecting the claim. Point out in writing to the contractor any neglect in submitting such information to the engineer.

119   Establish the circumstances and contractual basis

which the contractor considers justifies the claim. Discuss these with the contractor orally and in writing with a view to settling the question of liability. Hold formal meetings with the contractor to obtain any information needed to complete the claims register; discuss any difficulties encountered in obtaining information; discuss the merits of selected claims which have previously been discussed informally; discuss the need for measures which would reduce or remove the claim (e.g. Section IV); and request notification by the contractor of any claims not on record in writing. Take minutes of the proceedings.

120   Attempt to achieve as early a settlement of claims as is practicable. Do not make accommodations: accept the validity of any claim only as considered valid under the contract terms, even if the claim is or appears insignificant. In the case of large unresolved claims, attempt to persuade the promoter and the contractor to take all steps open to them under the contract in order to achieve a settlement at the earliest practicable date.

121   If the engineer, after consultation with the promoter, accepts the validity of any part of a claim, issue a Variation Order, Provisional Sum Order or P.C. Sum Order for any work and payment for which the promoter will be liable, or a letter of the type described in §1 (*k*(*iii*)) as appropriate. Enter the consequences in the system (§50).

122   Assist in settling any claims outstanding at the termination of the contract.

SECTION VII
FINANCIAL REVIEWS

123   Advise the promoter of substantial staff inputs needed to prepare a sound financial review and ask him to state time intervals between reviews. Provide the promoter with a financial review at agreed time intervals, consisting of the following.

Estimated final contract price

(*a*)   Known commitments

(*i*) the original contract price

(*ii*) estimated adjustments due to differences between originally billed quantities and final measured quantities, including costs due to dislocation of the programme (see 'Estimating costs and delays', Chapter 3)

(*iii*) itemized estimated adjustments due to Variations, including costs due to dislocation of the programme

(*iv*) itemized estimated adjustments to Provisional Sums, P.C. Sums and Provisional items, including costs due to dislocation of the programme

(*v*) estimated adjustments due to escalation

(*vi*) itemized estimated adjustments due to payments considered justified by the contract but for which the original measurement provides no method; see §1(*k*(*iii*))

(*vii*) any other adjustments considered necessary by the engineer, other than the following

(*b*) Other expected adjustments

(*i*) due to itemized expected Variations, including costs due to dislocation of the programme

(*ii*) due to itemized existing claims expected to prove valid, including any costs due to dislocation of the programme

(*iii*) due to itemized expected claims likely to prove valid, including any costs due to dislocation of the programme

(*iv*) an allowance for contingencies, including risk of claims proving to be justified

(*c*) Statement

(*i*) a short statement on claims considered by the engineer to be unjustified

(*ii*) a statement that the financial review does not include costs external to the contract

(*iii*) the basis of estimates

124   Ensure that estimated adjustments in the review are not conflicting (e.g. when Variation Orders, Provisional Sum

Orders, P.C. Sum Orders, Provisional Item Orders, or letters
(§1(*k*)) amend previous Orders or letters).

125   Estimate adjustments to the construction programme
on the basis described in Chapter 3 under 'Estimating costs and
delays'. The contract programme in use on site for stimulating
effort may be too optimistic regarding delays because it does
not adequately take account of this basis. If this is so, prepare a
simple bar-chart programme allowing for the engineer's
estimate of delays; that is, his practical assessment of future
progress without the adoption of any special measures to
expedite construction, other than any already agreed with the
contractor or ordered by the engineer. Check that the following
have been included in the financial review

(*a*)   the estimated costs of any special measures which have
been agreed or ordered for which the promoter is
considered liable

(*b*)   the estimated costs of any residual delay for which the
promoter is considered liable

(*c*)   any claim from the contractor for payment in excess of
these, due to delay

126   Point out to the promoter that the financial review
does not cover any costs other than those related to the
construction contract.

127   Discuss with promoter the allowance to be made for
contingencies; see §123 (*b*(*iv*)). Ensure that financial reviews
reach an appropriate management level in the promoter's
organization.

SECTION VIII
GENERAL FUNCTIONS

128   Obtain the promoter's nomination of his representative in matters related to the contract. Meet him as needed to
avoid misunderstanding and help each other.

129   Arrange regular meetings between the engineer's
representative and the promoter's representative for the site,
with the object of initiating any joint action required and of
dealing with it at site level if practicable.

130   Keep notes of any deficiencies of the control system as work proceeds and correct and up-date it as needed.

131   Check that the contractor maintains insurances required by the contract.

132   Record apparent deficiences in the contract documents as work proceeds, to enable any necessary amendments to be made in preparing future documents.

133   List programmes (§§5,8,9,10,27–31) and schedules (§§39,93) and arrange their safe and accessible keeping.

134   Prepare forecast of the engineer's representative's staff levels by category of staff.

135   Review staff functions and levels of staffing during construction and revise forecasts of staff needed (§82).

136   Prepare periodical progress reports from engineer to promoter and from engineer's representative to engineer.

137   Make arrangements ensuring that copies of all relevant correspondence are exchanged between the head and site offices.

138   Make provision for recovery from the promoter or contractor of additional costs to the engineer not otherwise provided for.

139   Check returns required from the contractor, including

(*a*)   progress reports and details of time lost
(*b*)   labour strength and labour difficulties
(*c*)   accident reports
(*d*)   equipment on site and details of breakdowns
(*e*)   materials orders placed and materials on site
(*f*)   short-term programme of work
(*g*)   records for payment purposes (e.g. time-and-materials records, details of estimated escalations)

140   Administer site office organization

(*a*)   assisting in review of staff salaries and wages
(*b*)   accounts, including

(*i*)   maintaining accounts
(*ii*)   payment of staff salaries and wages
(*iii*)   payment for office requirements

       (*iv*) maintaining engineer's insurances relevant to the office

       (*v*) assisting with other functions containing an accounting element (e.g. assisting in checking interim certificates)

(*c*) provision, maintenance and replacement as necessary of office facilities, equipment and services, including

       (*i*) heated, air-conditioned office accommodation as needed; furniture and equipment, including fire-proof cabinets for essential papers

       (*ii*) other equipment (e.g. surveying equipment)

       (*iii*) transport, including drivers

       (*iv*) printing and reproduction of documents, including drawings

       (*v*) telecommunications, including radio communication

       (*vi*) office cleaning and maintenance, and messenger services

       (*vii*) other facilities, equipment and services as needed (e.g. access to computer)

(*d*) clerical and secretarial services, including

       (*i*) correspondence services

       (*ii*) filing

       (*iii*) recording visits to site

       (*iv*) other general office services

141 Carry out the completion procedure as required by the contract and issue completion certificates.

3. Problems of construction supervision

Introduction

Problems arising in supervision can be classified as having the following characteristics.

(a) The treatments are immediately evident in referring to the control system for the contract.
(b) Treatments are not immediately evident but are provided for in the control system, usually by a combination of procedures.
(c) Explanation of control system procedures is needed.
(d) The problem has not been foreseen in preparing the control system.

The first need not be considered further. The specimen control system provides procedures for recognizing the last type of problem (SCS§§16,82) and for improving future control systems (SCS§130). No-one can foresee all eventualities in preparing a control system, however, and some omissions are bound to occur.

There are many problems of the second type and the combinations of procedures needed to treat them become clear in practice. Provided the form of system has not been allowed to grow cumbersome by unnecessarily perfectionist, legalistic, formal or technological additions over the years its use should be virtually automatic. For instance, if, inside a coffer-dam for a new dock, a hole had to be cut in permanent cut-off piling for temporary construction reasons, the danger of failing to seal the hole would be dealt with as follows.

(a) The staff of the engineer's representative would refer the proposal to him or his deputy (SCS§103).

27

(*b*)   The engineer's representative would obtain the contractor's proposal, including sealing the hole.

(*c*)   When the engineer's representative considered the proposal acceptable, he would confirm it in writing (SCS§1(*k*(*i*))).

(*d*)   Copies of the letter would be passed to the site engineer in charge of the master copy of the contract details and the quantity surveyor (SCS§3) and the work to be done would be indicated on the permanent and temporary works drawings (SCS§1(*b*) and (*g*)).

(*e*)   In clearing the master copy dock drawings before flooding the coffer-dam, the reminder to seal the hole could not be missed. It would not be left to memory or inspection.

(*f*)   All communications would be in the simplest effective form.

Similar procedures provide means for dealing with many other supervision problems.

Consideration of problems of the third type and explanations of control system procedures related to them follow. They consist mainly of enlargements on the provisions in Section IV of the specimen control system 'Alterations and delays'. Reference to that Section will be useful in reading the following.

Identification of construction problems

A legitimate objective of the promoter or the contractor will be to obtain the most favourable outcome of a contract to himself by methods not in conflict with the contract. Neither will have cause to complain provided the contract is fair and each has a reasonable regard for the other's interest.

A control system based on the specimen system will signal measures to be taken by the engineer which will serve both the promoter's and the contractor's reasonable aims. Many of these measures are straight forward in application. Some, however, may be difficult. They include those dealing with the following problems causing costs and delays

(*a*)   the effects of adverse labour relations

(b) alterations requested by the promoter to improve the project
(c) alterations thought necessary by the engineer's design or site staff to improve the project (e.g. to introduce a more modern type of construction)
(d) alterations thought necessary by the engineer for other reasons (e.g. purely technical)
(e) alterations requested by the contractor to reduce his time and/or costs of construction
(f) adverse physical conditions (including artificial obstructions)
(g) inadequacy of equipment or materials
(h) inadequacy of the engineer's or contractor's management or labour; for instance inadequate provision of numbers of each required skill

One of the greatest problems which the engineer and contractor may have to face may be the background against which they are both working. Situations will exist where they will know that they are putting effort into a project which will probably not be worthwhile. The dilemma posed by scepticism and the need for commitment, though silent and barely recognized, may have to be resolved. The presence of disruption due to industrial action, itself an assertion of opinions that other interests are more important than continuing work on a project, may add further doubt and discouragement.

Other disincentives exist against attacking difficult construction problems with vigour. The engineer's tendency is to put the achievement of a satisfactory finished physical product before questions of cost, purely as a result of his professional training and outlook. He will often be in a position where delays and additional costs will be of less damage to him than defects in the quality of design and construction. The contractor may also consider that some delays will cause him no irretrievable loss and that efforts to minimize them would add to his costs. He may also naturally be resistant to admitting that the construction methods, equipment or construction staff planned by himself are inadequate.

The engineer may recognize the onset or existence of

problems in reviewing the programme and progress, in inspection of the works, or in other normal activities of supervision. It may not be easy to see which problems will be transient and which must be dealt with quickly to forestall unacceptable increases in construction costs or delay. Identifying the causes of a problem may prove more troublesome. Attempts to forecast problem circumstances of which there is little present evidence, is by definition difficult.

A deliberate effort at foresight by taking a view of normal sources of difficulty and eliminating unfounded suspicions may be helpful. A promoter's tendency to request an excess of alterations may be recognized by examining his past record; similarly a designer's tendency to generate improved designs may be foreseen; review of the original site investigation borings and tests, based on experience gained in opening up foundations in the early stages of construction, may point to potential troubles; a hydraulic problem in breakwater port construction may be recognized by observing wave characteristics during construction and reviewing with the designers their significance to the completed port wave characteristics; local knowledge can be acquired (fishermen have correctly advised engineers of wave action affecting construction methods at a certain season). These and similar projections may warn of future trouble, but, in general major problems do not give much notice of their arrival.

General signs of the existence or approach of difficulties are a claim from the contractor; oral notification by the contractor of circumstances which he considers might call for additional payment or time; or the contractor's reply to a request at a claims meeting for confirmation that he has no claims to add to the existing claims list — a reply which, when minuted in the early stages of the contract period, may add some colour to the minutes (SCS§119(*e*)).

At any time during the contract period the engineer will have a list of existing or foreseen problems. He should classify them according to a rough judgement of the order of cost of resolving and of not resolving each problem, and should indicate a tentative opinion whether costs are likely to be to the promoter or the contractor. The timing for dealing with each problem should be indicated. Classifying the problems on this basis signifies both an intention not to be hasty in judging the validity of claims, and the engineer's concern to minimize costs which may fall upon the contractor, provided that the promoter's interests are not adversely affected.

Alterations contemplated by the promoter or the engineer

The engineer's methods of considering proposals for such alterations and implementing approved proposals are described in the specimen control system (SCS§§43–54). They provide for attempts to discuss the feasibility of alterations with the contractor on the basis of 'what appears to be best for the project irrespective of liability' where there is a possibility of the contractor being liable for the cost of part of the alterations. The contractor may have reservations because his liability may be appreciable or he may fear that it will prove so. The specimen control system provides for identifying technically feasible alterations, selecting the most favourable or rejecting all, and implementing any selected alteration. It provides for using economy evaluation where important questions of the financial feasibility of proposed alterations are concerned.

Alterations proposed by the contractor

Measures for dealing with proposed alterations of this type will have to ensure that the expected economy of the project (i.e. to the promoter) is not affected adversely by an accepted proposal. The measures include detailed procedures for checking and amending proposals (SCS§§55–67). These need no further explanation.

Other construction problems

Many other difficulties, including adverse physical conditions, inadequacies of equipment or materials, problems as to the suitability of management or labour, and delays due to adverse labour relations are overcome in the field in the normal course of supervision and works management. The engineer should take trouble to promote co-operation between himself and the contractor and particularly their site staffs, because each will have skills the other will need and respect. Both he and the contractor should recognize that the divergence between their objectives is essential to achieving a project satisfactory to the promoter. They should work on the understanding that co-operation, as it is expressed in the specimen control system, and divergence of objectives are far more effective than fixed positions of divergence alone. Discussion need not be greatly restricted as it can be based on the understanding that opinions will be expressed without prejudice to liability, although this will not remove all reservations. Under the system suggested in the specimen, no valid claim would be initiated by these efforts and procedures for identifying claims which would arise otherwise would be provided for (SCS§119 (e)).

There are various views among engineers and contractors as to the lengths to which the engineer should go in attempting to resolve construction difficulties and control delays. Investigation, analysis and examination of alternative courses of action, preferably in collaboration with the contractor, can offer savings to the promoter and the contractor in excess of the staff and other costs involved. Action of this kind does not increase the risk of liability for additional costs. The engineer may apply method study or operational research; he may use the design engineer's special ability to devise alterations to the permanent works; he may offer previous experience of a method of construction; or he may make other enquiries which have a bearing on some particular difficulty (for instance, a promoter might be able to offer assistance in expediting Customs clearance of shipped materials). In short, he can offer the results of any investigation and analysis to the contractor without instruction and without prejudice to the contract. The presentation of objective evidence and outlines of possible treatments will often assist both himself and the contractor to arrive at possible courses of action. The staff input concerned will not be excessive because the application of the methods will be confined to major problems and the skills needed within the staffs' normal knowledge. The staff input will also be offset by avoiding delays in construction and the input needed to deal with them.

The engineer may as previously described form a tentative

opinion that a particular problem can be treated solely by means of an alteration to the existing design, find the opinion to be correct and arrange for the alteration to be carried out. He may, however, realize from the outset that a design alteration alone would not be satisfactory or may discover this when various alternatives are considered. The reason for this will in general be physical conditions, problems of equipment, materials, management, suitability of labour, or the effects of adverse labour relations, in which case he will look for other treatments.

Though the effects of a problem may be evident, the causes of it may be obscure. As an exercise in clarification, the engineer should write down a short account of the circumstances attending the problem. Discussion of this with relevant members of his site and design staff and with the contractor, will assist in planning further action. If the engineer considers that normal methods will not deal adequately with the problem, he can prepare a simple programme for investigation which may be needed, including as he thinks necessary

(*a*)   time to be allowed for discussions with the people concerned before taking further action

(*b*)   method study of, or operational research into, operations causing difficulty

(*c*)   additional site investigations

(*d*)   special tactics (e.g. a temporary switch of works management)

(*e*)   the services of technical or operations advisors

(*f*)   trial of proposed treatments

(*g*)   the latest date for completing outline details of technically feasible alternative treatments of the problem

The engineer and the contractor will in the normal course of construction discuss the problem on the basis of their site staff's efforts, investigations and analysis, and their own inspections of the circumstances. Their intention should be to identify the best option, when a number of alternative treatments may be technically feasible, some at first sight more preferable to the engineer than the contractor. The engineer will wish to establish an objective view and may attempt this by empirically applying the standard 'what appears to be best for the project irrespective of liability' to the comparison of alternatives. However, both engineer and contractor will have arrived at some tentative judgement on the apportionment of liability for the cost of any treatment needed. The engineer will, for each alternative, have prepared preliminary estimates of the cost to the promoter, including costs of any delay, and forecasts of effects on the contract programme; and the contractor will have made similar estimates of costs to himself and forecasts of programme effects. In the great majority of cases, the choice of treatments will be very limited and estimates and forecasts approximate.

It is important that, in arriving at a solution, the engineer and contractor look for a selection which will be optimal to both the promoter and the contractor. This will be a matter of technical judgement and sometimes economy evaluation.

There will be few problems, even on a large contract, which will not answer to one or more of the preceding treatments. The adoption or rejection of alterations proposed by the promoter, the engineer or the contractor, solutions formulated jointly by the contractor and the engineer in the field, occasional simple method study, simple special tactics, and toleration of some minor chronic situations of no more than nuisance effect can overcome most difficulties; though some of the treatments may be only partially effective and may come rather late.

The few problems which prove more difficult to despatch generally include one or two which may be damaging to the project economy, though not such as to cause the parties pain at the time or in retrospect. However, the engineer can expect one or perhaps two problems which are very difficult to treat, and which, if not treated, are certain to prove costly to the promoter or contractor or both. The engineer will hope to recognize these serious problems at an early stage, and preferably before undertaking any investigation which may prove inadequate. He may have trouble in doing this; contractors and engineers often achieve their ends over apparently serious problems without resorting to formal programmes of investigation. This does not lessen the need to recognize serious problems which would not respond to such treatment, and to do so as soon as is practicable. When a problem is recognizably of the very difficult kind, it may be difficult also to identify and programme the investigations needed to decide on a treatment. Discussion with the contractor may not be immediately productive because he also will be having the same difficulties and will be wary of costly measures for which he may prove to be liable. The engineer and contractor will probably be able to agree on method study and consideration of special tactics likely to be of assistance, but may differ if the engineer suggests extensive site investigation or a costly trial of a proposed treatment.

By this time, discussion of the subject on the basis of what appears to be best for the project irrespective of liability may have become a memory and interchanges, non-productive. If this is so, the engineer should record the history of the problem, delays attributable to it, the present position, efforts made to deal with the situation and an outline description of any investigatory measures he and the contractor have suggested to identify possible treatments. He should present this to the contractor with a request for his comments and proposals. The engineer's suggestions may include extensive investigatory measures and the contractor may offer little in the way of comment or proposal, except an assertion of his opinion with regard to liability. He may well, however, offer constructive suggestions, possibly measures likely to prove more effective than the engineer's. In any case, the engineer should have in mind construction costs (including costs of delay) and delay in completion, and should have arrived at some opinion as to the probabilities of the cost falling upon the promoter or the contractor. He must never be other than fully committed to identifying a satisfactory treatment. Even if liability seems certain to fall upon the contractor, he must assist in minimizing the inevitable non-recoverable costs to the promoter of delay in commissioning the project. He should also assist in minimizing the contractor's costs, provided that costs to the promoter are also minimized.

If the engineer and contractor can at this stage agree on the investigatory measures to be taken to identify treatment, either agreeing on liability for the measures or without prejudice to the contract, they will put them in hand. If they cannot agree, then the engineer may again review his and the contractor's proposals and decide whether to accept the contractor's, to reconsider his own (possibly with additional expert opinion) or to insist that his own proposals are carried out. At some time during the negotiations, and with the minimum of delay, the engineer must decide on the investigatory measures to be taken. So far as these agree with the contractor's proposals he should record the agreement and so far as they do not, he should instruct the contractor. Neither the agreement nor the instruction will prevent the contractor from undertaking other investigatory measures provided that they are undertaken in accordance with the contract.

The engineer is unlikely to have much difficulty in deciding whether or not to instruct the contractor if he considers the measures the most effective that he, after consultation with the contractor, can devise. The proposals will be for purely investigatory measures and the engineer will almost certainly be able to formulate them so as to avoid interference with the contractor's operations. On the other hand, the cost to the promoter of not treating a major problem would be high (about £0.25 million per month of delay in commissioning a £20 million project, apart from any additional construction costs for which he might be liable). Investigatory measures will therefore cost little in relation to the consequences of not treating the problem. If the engineer is satisfied that the investigatory measures, even if they prove not fully effective, will at least be justified by providing improvements in treating the problem, he should instruct the contractor to put them into effect.

The investigatory measures will have been prepared and ordered on the assumption that the contractor will continue to carry out any other action he has proposed and the engineer agreed, and that attention will be given to the problem in the course of normal supervision and works management.

Treatment of the problem will almost always be needed urgently and the engineer and contractor should examine the investigation's results from the time they begin to come forward, together with results obtained in the normal course of supervision and works management. In oral discussion the engineer should not deviate from those facts, analyses or proposals which he can clearly establish, nor pursue matters obscured by intractable conflicts of interest. He should present a working paper supporting his case, without prejudice to liability, and leave the contractor to examine it; the working paper should be as short as possible and in basic form such as hand-written reports and copies of calculations. He should ask the contractor to do likewise.

The outcome of the investigations will be one or more technically feasible treatments, which may include

(*a*) alterations to the permanent works
(*b*) changes in equipment or materials
(*c*) rearrangement and perhaps strengthening of the contractor's or engineer's staff or of labour
(*d*) changes in construction methods
(*e*) other feasible treatments devised by experience and ingenuity
(*f*) any combination of such treatments

Technically feasible treatments of the problem may entail substantial future costs to the promoter, possibly including costs due to delay in commissioning. The chosen treatment can be unnecessarily costly to the contractor. Costs to either will depend on liability. Evaluations of the financial effects of feasible treatments on the promoter and the contractor on the basis of discounted costs and benefits may be needed (SCS§78).

The selection of the treatment to be carried out should be considered by the promoter, engineer and contractor together. It should not be hurried nor conducted from fixed positions as it will result in a major decision affecting both the promoter's and contractor's returns from the contract considerably. Agreement on a first selection does not contradict this advice as that selection may be wrong.

Action which may have to be taken in the event of continued disagreement between promoter, engineer and contractor on the treatment to be adopted is not considered in detail here. It will vary considerably according to the circumstances applying to different cases. In practice the method of treatment is unlikely to be a matter of great contention if its selection is based on adequate investigation and analysis. The contractor's agreement with the selection of a treatment will not, however, signify his acceptance of liability for additional costs or delay attributable to the treatment, and it may be necessary as a matter of urgency for the engineer and the promoter to come to a decision on important claims rising from the treatment.

The time taken from recognizing a problem as one requiring special treatment to implementing the treatment should be minimized by starting work on the preparation of contract details for the treatment as soon as the investigation has provided sufficient information to enable a choice of treatment to be made, and starting construction work as soon as sufficient contract details are available. Price negotiation will probably have to be done later. All other work needed to identify technically feasible treatments and select the preferred treatment should be carried out during this time. The engineer's staff input will be that needed to assist the contractor in any method study or operational research; to prepare specifications for any site investigation, trial treatments or other investigatory measures, jointly with the contractor; to prepare treatment details required of the engineer; and to supervise additional site work.

Implementation of alterations

An alteration may be taken as any change in the master copy of the contract details requiring the engineer's order, agreement or approval, including any change in the permanent works, materials, workmanship, construction methods or programmes; and any change in the contractor's staff or labour, or construction equipment requiring the engineer's order, agreement or approval. Any method of conveying the engineer's orders, agreements and approvals to the contractor must conform with the contract and cover both work to be done and payment conditions. It should be an aid to stating the engineer's intentions clearly and maintaining consistency of practice on a contract and generally within the engineer's organization in a wide variety of circumstances.

During the course of construction, the engineer will have to make decisions on action to be taken and interim payments to be made to the contractor, leaving disputes to be settled by claims and other negotiatory procedures during the contract period, or later by the appropriate provisions made in the conditions of contract. Means for conveying the action to be taken to the contractor and for recording the position on payment may include

(*a*) Variation Orders
(*b*) Provisional and P.C. Sum Orders and Provisional Item Orders[1]
(*c*) letters issued by the engineer to the contractor
  (*i*) recording any agreement with the contractor enabling him to deviate from the master copy of the contract details, on condition that it entails no additional costs to the promoter, or that it offers a reduction in his costs
  (*ii*) ordering or approving measures for which the engineer, in disagreement with the contractor, considers no additional payment due
  (*iii*) providing a method of payment where the engineer considers payment justified by the contract but for which the specified measurement provides no method

If the 'ICE Conditions of Contract' (Fifth Edition) are in force, some delays may be treated under Clause 46 which states, *inter alia,* 'If for any reason which does not entitle the Contractor to an extension of time the rate of progress of the Works or any Section is at any time in the opinion of the Engineer too slow to ensure completion by the prescribed time or extended time for completion, the Engineer shall so notify

---

[1]Orders for work which has been included in the bill of quantities as provisional because the decision whether or not to order the work has not been made. The work has been detailed in the original contract document and prices for it agreed.

the Contractor in writing and the Contractor shall thereupon take such steps as are necessary and the Engineer may approve to expedite progress so as to complete the Works or such Section by the prescribed time or extended time. The Contractor shall not be entitled to any additional payment for taking such steps.' In this case the Engineer would need a further form of letter

> (*iv*) informing the contractor of his approval or rejection of proposals under Clause 46 from the contractor to expedite progress

In any particular case, all work required and payment to be made may be included in one Variation Order, one Provisional Sum Order, one P.C. Sum Order, or one Provisional Item order, under the heading of the main type of Order concerned, and this Order may include any required provision under section (c) on page 39; or if only the provisions of section (c) were needed, they may be made in one letter.

There is an objection to the method. One may, for instance, find that a Variation Order about to be issued alters various previous Orders or letters. In this case a perfectionist solution would be to divide the contemplated Variation Order into separate Orders or letters to be issued under the heading of each relevant previous Order or letter. This method would have the advantage of simplifying the preparation of the financial review but it would at times lead to complications. The engineer will usually avoid such complications by issuing one Variation Order complete in itself, referring in it to previous Orders or letters which are amended by it. In preparing the financial review he should then examine and correct existing adjustments in the review as they are affected by any Order or letter issued since the last review was prepared (SCS§124).

The engineer will often have to write to the contractor to arrange for alterations to be carried out and payment to be made. The specimen control system (SCS§§49,50) suggests a standard method of doing this and of making arrangements for subsequent supervision.

The use of letters in certain circumstances instead of Orders is recommended for the following reasons: first, they remind the experienced or less-experienced engineer that he is dealing with agreements, approvals, provisions or rejections of proposals, and not with orders for alterations; second, not being orders, they should not be implemented as any of the forms of Order; and third, letters of this type will have to be issued whether or not they are recognized, and it is better to issue them under a system which provides for filing them in the master contract details and which signals other supervisory action to be taken (SCS§50). The recognition of agreements, approvals, provisions and rejections, as distinct from Orders, is applicable to all conditions of contract, and a useful clarification when there are language difficulties.

Estimating costs and delays

Estimates of construction costs to the promoter of any changes in the permanent works, temporary works, materials, equipment, staff, labour etc. for which the promoter might be liable are needed for pricing bills of quantities, considering the feasibility of alterations and measures for overcoming construction difficulties, valuing claims and forecasting final costs. The costs of changes made during construction are affected by delays imposed by the changes on all work affected by the changes, due to dislocation of a co-ordinated construction programme. The ratio, increment of dislocation (and therefore of delay) to increment of change, remains fairly constant until a critical level of total change is reached. It then increases continually with further change. If the changes are many, large delays will be incurred by small changes and costs will follow suit. The estimation of the costs of changes should be controlled by the engineer and (unless he himself is an expert) by an estimating expert, usually a quantity surveyor. The estimates should include costs assuming no contract programme dislocation; costs of any measures which may be necessary to offset delay; and costs due to any residual dislocation of the contract programme.

Neglect of these costs may be the cause of heavy unforeseen cost increases or delays in completion and project commissioning. The engineer should advise the promoter of the full estimated cost of any significant proposed change and of any

41

expected significant delay in completion (SCS§§43,44,51–54, 78). The financial review and a version of the contract programme, both restricted to the engineer's and the promoter's view, should reflect these estimates as well as cost and programme effects of less significant changes (SCS§§123, 125).

Exceptional contract settlements

The view has been expressed that contractual claims are sometimes settled between promoters and contractors by means which are outside the terms of the contracts which are supposed to represent the whole agreement between them, and that such settlements vitiate the attempts to control costs provided in the contract terms. Some element of doubt often exists in interpreting contracts and the circumstances concerned in disputes, and settlements may have reflected the doubt. Certainly, however, settlements have been made as the result of inadmissible pressure or incentives applied by a contractor to a promoter or vice versa, sometimes itself motivated by external pressure exerted on one or the other or both. The effect of such a situation on engineering control is to attack the measures needed for financial control, extending quickly to measures needed for control of workmanship and speed of construction.

The Author has seen no definitive report on the frequency of contractual misadventures nor on comprehensive measures for avoiding them. Whatever the frequency, the individual engineer's reaction to such a situation must be to make the best use of his supervisory role under the contract with or without the promoter's or contractor's co-operation, making every effort to redress the situation and regarding the lack of co-operation as just another difficulty to be dealt with as provided for in the contract. In the last resort he may judge it better to withdraw and pursue his efforts from an independent position. This troublesome process is a situation which some engineers have to face.

The engineer's site staff

Engineering supervision is the work of the engineer, the site

staff, head office design staff and specialized head office staff
or external advisors. Any use of specialized staff or external
advisors' services would be the engineer's decision. The site
staff will be required to supervise construction as prescribed in
the contract and further detailed in the control system and this
will imply the existence of sufficient staff at various levels
experienced in the classes of work. The engineer's allocation of
responsibilities to himself (apart from his natural overall
responsibility) and head office staff, and to his representative
on site and his staff, will reflect his policy on the division of
responsibility and the confidence that he has in the site staff.

The control system should provide means for maintaining
the minimum required levels of staff, and this entails both a
definition of what the engineer considers adequate, and review
and adjustment of the staff's work to provide that degree of
adequacy. The specimen system gives some guidance on
minimizing staff inputs consistent with adequacy
(SCS§§8,82,86,109,113,135). Site office facilities should be of
sufficient size to allow the site staff to work without
congestion; furniture, equipment and services (e.g. drawing and
document filing facilities, document and drawing reproduction,
telecommunications, calculators, and access to computer)
should be adequate to avoid time spent on subordinate
activities.

There is a general method of controlling staff inputs and
improving the quality of supervision. It consists of identifying
existing or proposed staff inputs which may not be worthwhile,
writing down the advantages and disadvantages of the inputs
(almost on the back of an envelope, initially at least), and
evaluating these in the simplest practical way. Many existing or
proposed staff inputs may be judged worthwhile or not on this
basis, without formal quantification. In more questionable
cases or where larger staff inputs are concerned, the methods of
evaluation set out in the Appendix may be used.

When at the outset of construction the engineer has decided
on the division of functions between himself and the engineer's
representative on site he will need to provide the latter with a
written statement of the powers delegated to him. The conditions of contract will usually provide him with wide discretion

in this respect and it is suggested that he might appoint only engineer's representatives to whom he is prepared to delegate wide powers, for the following reasons.

(*a*) The engineer will to a large extent be absent from the site and the engineer's representative's responsibilities will therefore of necessity be wide.

(*b*) The engineer's representative should have the challenge necessary for his satisfaction as an experienced engineer, and to his growth as an engineer.

(*c*) The engineer's representative should be encouraged to establish a similar policy of delegation among his staff.

4. Economy evaluation, method study and operational research

Economy evaluation

Economy evaluation may be taken as meaning the comparison of alternative courses of action by analysis of commercial costs and benefits attributable to the courses of action. A text on supervision is not the place for detailed consideration of its techniques any more than of other specialized engineering subjects. Simple evaluation, such as that considered here, is, however, enough for dealing with all but exceptional problems, and for recognizing such problems and the consequent need for more specialized advice.[1]

Methods of evaluation. To the promoter the effects on the economy of a project of any decision taken during construction are not exhibited only by changes in the contract price and the completion date, but by the flow of all costs and benefits attributable to the decision to the end of the project's useful life. As all decisions will be made in answer to a problem it may be taken that the consideration of decisions is consideration of treatments of problems whether they are alterations to the permanent works, temporary works, equipment, management or construction methods.

In general the project economy will be exhibited by the year-by-year flow of the following project costs and benefits to the end of the project's useful life

(*a*) capital costs, including

(*i*) payments to the contractor under the construction contract

---

[1]Relevant sections of *Principles of engineering economy* by Eugene L. Grant and W. Grant Ireson (ref. 2), are very clear.

45

(*ii*)   costs to the promoter of any other contract for goods and services needed to complete the project, including consultants' services

(*iii*) the promoter's direct costs attributable to the project (e.g. acquisition of land, administration costs)

(*iv*)   other costs of commissioning the project (e.g. staff training)

(*v*)   replacements during the project's life

(*vi*)   residual value of the project assets at the end of the project's life

(*b*)   operating costs of the project, including maintenance and excluding depreciation

(*c*)   income from the project

(*d*)   any other benefits to the promoter (e.g. value of research attributable to the project)

The effect of any treatment will be represented by year-by-year changes in these costs and benefits attributable solely to the treatment. If these are discounted at a selected rate of interest (usually the rate of return expected by the promoter) to the time of making the decision, the result will be the estimated present value of the treatment. The economy of alternative treatments, including the alternative of taking no action, may be judged by comparing the present values of each.

In selecting a suitable treatment, the promoter, engineer and contractor may consider both the present values and the effects of alternative treatments on the public interest which have not been quantified, such as effects on the environment and safety of personnel.

Uses of evaluation. In dealing with alterations and delays, the specimen system signals discussions with the promoter on the need for evaluation. Evaluation of alternative feasible treatments would be indicated by expected changes in output or in operating (including maintenance) costs of the completed project, if one or other of the possible alternatives were selected, or if selection of one or other would incur appreciable delay in completion. In such cases, the financially most favourable alternative could not be selected purely by a comparison of estimated capital costs.

There are cases where the promoter can transfer his selection of treatment from his first choice to another because he would incur only small additional costs yet permit the contractor large savings. Where this possibility exists, the promoter, engineer and contractor should analyse the costs and benefits of alternative treatments to the contractor as well as the promoter. Estimating the costs and benefits to the promoter and the contractor would require a judgement of their liabilities and the contractor might not agree with the engineer's judgement. The prospect of a bargain, however, would be an incentive to both to reach agreement. On occasion it may be useful if the engineer and the contractor consider the effect on estimated present values of the probability of their liability judgements being wrong.[2] In all cases the engineer should take the question of liability into account in reaching a decision and be clear in recording the decision as an Order or a letter of agreement or approval as appropriate.

Examples of various uses of economy evaluation appear in the Appendix (Examples 1–3) and it may be noted that useful results can be obtained by simple means. There are two levels of evaluation, one more detailed than the other. Example 1 may be considered something of a 'set-piece' evaluation, though an elementary one, and Examples 2 and 3 as 'little' evaluations. Recognition of the need for set-piece evaluation is a matter for the engineer, the promoter's representative for the project and the contractor. The engineer can make use of the little evaluation in arriving at many decisions, and not least among its advantages may be the discovery that a problem thought to be of minor importance is or may be critical, and vice versa.

There is no danger of over-using cost–benefit methods, provided that they are not a fascination and end in themselves, as limitations of their uses are easily recognized. It is more difficult to avoid unnecessary sophistication as techniques of risk analysis and optimization do improve decisions and have their own attractions; in any construction problem other than

[2] See *Risk analysis in project appraisal* by Louis Y. Poliquen. (ref. 4)

the exceptional, the improvement will be no more than marginal, and usually submerged by uncertainties.

The estimation of construction costs and delays for the comparison of alternative treatments need not be detailed. More detailed estimates of these costs and delays for the selected treatment will be prepared later, and, if as a result it appears that the estimates used in the comparison were too wide of the mark, the comparison can be rerun, using adjusted estimates. It is unlikely that the selection will be changed as it depends largely on relative rather than absolute estimates of construction costs and delays.

Method study and operational research

Method study is well defined and illustrated by R. M. Currie (ref. 1) and has wide applications in bringing order to a complicated system of operations. A simple case of its use is described in Example 7 of the Appendix. Sasieni, Yaspan and Friedman (ref. 5) deal with basic operational research. Its aspects useful to the engineer in construction are network planning, queuing analysis and mathematical programming. Network planning is in general use in construction and a case of queuing analysis is given in Example 4 of the Appendix.

In general the contractor and the engineer will have a choice of the following measures in dealing with a construction problem

(a) normal and special efforts of works management
(b) the measures referred to in §§70 and 73 of the specimen control system, that is

    (i) method study or operational research
    (ii) additional site investigations
    (iii) special tactics
    (iv) the services of technical or operations advisors
    (v) trials of proposed treatments

The question whether method study or operational research should be undertaken will depend on the benefits to the promoter or contractor in this context. This is a question of analysis and judgement and one on which the engineer and contractor can reach a fair degree of agreement, even if it is not admitted. The question of liability for the costs of study or research and that of who should carry it out will depend on the contract terms and on efficiency.

The use of the methods need not be confined to problems of particular difficulty, of large construction contracts or where there is a high risk of heavy losses or delays, as it may be the cheapest way of treating a problem which is none of these. A decision whether or not to use the methods should depend simply on opinion as to their justification in terms of benefits to the promoter.

The need for method study and operational research. In some cases method study is clearly indicated, as in Example 7 of the Appendix, and the same may be true of operational research, as in Example 4 of the Appendix. In such cases, specialist advice on the study or research will be unnecessary or limited. Indications, however, will often not be clear and, in considering the whole package of measures needed to deal with a problem, the engineer and contractor will usually start off with little idea of the value of method study or operational research. They will have only

(*a*) a doubt as to the effectiveness of measures other than method study or operational research, based on knowledge and experience

(*b*) a firm opinion as to the choice between method study and operational research, should either be worthwhile

(*c*) a firm opinion as to the choice between network planning, queuing analysis and mathematical programming, on the basis of experience of network planning, the waiting-line characteristics of queuing problems, and the optimization of transportation allocation in mathematical programming[3]

If method study is under consideration, the engineer, contractor and method study specialist can make the decision whether or not to undertake the study, and design and carry it

[3]The contractor, but rarely the engineer, may be interested in other aspects of operational research, such as inventory control and replacement.

out, without great risk of misunderstandings between the engineer and contractor on the one side and the specialist on the other. The engineer and contractor will clearly understand method study in practice as it is directly connected with actual situations and events. This is not necessarily true of operational research, where generalized mathematics is used to model a practical problem. Initially the engineer and contractor may not be fully acquainted with the mathematics and the specialist not used to the practical circumstances. They must close the gap in communication if the risk of seriously distorting solutions is to be avoided.

Study and research should be carried out to a well-defined plan, including a programme and planned staff and any other inputs. If at any stage further work is considered unjustified, the cost of work done should not exceed the cost of the study or research to date as it should not have interfered with other work. The benefit will be useful information collected and conclusions reached before discontinuation.

The use of method study and operational research to the engineer in construction supervision should be placed in perspective. The Author can only quote his own experience. It is that small-scale method studies (Appendix Example 7) are frequently useful and larger-scale studies occasionally so (in his case about seven, including one much greater). Operational research on a scale similar to that of Appendix Example 4, and excluding the more frequent use of network planning, has been useful to the Author on a dozen or so occasions. The experience covers about 20 years of close association with construction and increasing awareness of study and research.

5. The practice of supervision

Policy

A competent control system is not a set of rules which, if followed to the letter, will deliver the benefits of efficient supervision. The efficiency of supervision depends on the engineer's interpretation of the system and the effectiveness with which he implements it. It also depends on the engineer's effectiveness in recognizing difficulties not provided for in the system and dealing with them — another aspect of implementation. The practice of supervision is the provision of the necessary qualities of implementation.

Visualizing for oneself the qualities of implementation which, given a competent control system, will create efficient supervision is not something one often tries to do, and conveying what one visualizes is an even less frequent occupation. The language of 'leadership' and 'decision making' is not illuminating. Detailed case studies have little impact in expressing the pressures of practice — reading *The murders in the Rue Morgue* falls short of finding a corpse in the chimney. Attempts to describe the engineering qualities needed are not useful. Ingenuity, judgement and tenacity are hard to assess and convey, and attempts to do so inevitably involve distinctions from deviousness and ruthlessness, especially when the latter have obvious short-term advantages.

At times the Author has tried, by observation, to recognize qualities which characterize competent supervising engineers, with foreseeable lack of success. The best supervising engineers, when asked how they operate, usually provide a criticism of incompetence and an iteration of the mundane techniques generally in use — planning, programming, day-to-day supervising etc. They have little conception of abilities they possess naturally. The observer will obtain a strong impression

51

of determination, interest and adherence to facts, but such processes as the early identification of problems, and, above all, the making of rapid and at least satisfactory decisions on short-term action will not be clear. Supervising engineers may explain these processes in detail to members of their site staff but this is not often done.

Having examined these surpisingly unhelpful options, it seems that one can do no better than consider what the engineer's implementation policies should be in treating difficult situations, including foreseeing them. Fortunately, most of the control system procedures are matters of engineering routine; that is, occasionally exigent and usually requiring engineering knowledge and experience, but rarely producing major implementation problems. The critical areas of activity lie in questions of the safety of the works, major construction problems and claims attributable to them.

A prime policy in effective implementation is concentration on activities necessary to fulfil the spirit of the control system. The system should convey this meaning, but it may be necessary to read it from time to time to inhibit tendencies to drift into non-productive detail, such as excessive inspection, setting-out, measurement of work done, reporting, maintaining diaries and so on.

Various procedures for foreseeing problems affecting the safety of works on a particular contract are set out in Section II of the specimen control system. The procedures would be of a similar kind for different classes of work. Whatever the case procedures for foreseeing safety problems should, as far as is practicable, be signalled in the control system, including a constant review of the question whether all that was expected during design is likely to be realized in practice (SCS§16). Section II of the specimen control system makes provision also for reviewing other questions as to the realization of important design intentions not strictly questions of safety (e.g. accretion and wave action, SCS§§9,10). The policy of implementation must be scepticism and the expectation of unforeseen trouble. The engineer should check design data against actual conditions made available in opening out the site, and design assumptions made deliberately or implicitly. He should be wary of the existence of hidden problems, including situations in which construction methods lead to dangers (Appendix Example 5). The engineer's representative will have the opportunity of considering these questions daily.

Construction risks do not cause engineers fear and there are dangers of complacency. Reviews and discussions (SCS§16), which should be regarded as horror sessions, will have more success in generating engineering curiosity and interest, which will serve assurance of safety well. The engineer should, however, be wary of those who pin all their faith on original designs, or take the presence of risk too lightly.

The engineer should never adopt a neutral, uniformedly critical or unconstructively critical attitude towards the contractor who has a construction problem, nor believe that he has no responsibility in relation to it. Short of prejudice to liability, he and his staff should regard the problem as their own and do everything practical to help the contractor create a solution from his talents in works management. He should also, as may be necessary, adopt and press the procedures described in Section IV of the specimen system as far as the conditions of contract permit. The 'ICE Conditions of Contract' (Fifth Edition) are positive and even-handed in this respect and most other standard terms of contract provide for the necessary powers. In the interests of the promoter, the engineer has usually, therefore, no option but to take reasonable action to assist in solving construction problems, using, as necessary, all his powers under the contract. He will be able to take reasonable action only if he has investigated and analysed the problem. Section IV of the specimen control system provides for action on this basis and continuous consultation with the contractor.

The engineer and site engineers will be cautious about taking action under Section IV which might subsequently prove to be non-productive, particularly when they are not well-versed in the techniques of the action to be taken, or when the action is opposed by their colleagues or the contractor and failure would be obvious. The use of the method study element of work study is a case in point. The decision to use the technique should be made by the engineer, if necessary and probably after consultation between site engineers and an expert on method study, preferably as applied to construction processes. It should then be put in hand, if necessary with advice, without further reservation. A similar policy should be adopted in taking any other action under Section IV which might prove to be non-productive, provided that the decision to take it has been made on a sound basis.

In implementing the control system as a whole, the engineer should not be deterred, nor allow his staff to be deterred, by objections which are not convincingly supported. This will include objections made by the promoter, the contractor, members of his staff or himself. His only concession to such objections should be reference to expert advice on the contract if the objections are based on contractual interpretation. Attempts at withdrawal of co-operation should be dealt with, first by consultation, then if necessary by the use of his powers under the contract.

When the first major difference of opinion with the contractor takes place, it should be made clear to him that the engineer, in taking action which the contractor may not like, will be taking considerable care to avoid infringing the contractor's operations. It should also be made clear that he intends to take any action within his powers under the contract which he considers necessary. These will include powers in relation to Variations, the quality of materials and workmanship, payment to be made, construction methods and equipment, steps necessary to expedite progress, and changes in the contractor's staff. The contractor will not be favourably disposed towards this. He will probably be to some extent offended by discussion and criticism of his means and methods of construction, and may resist it. It can help if the engineer can point to previous evidence of his policy of recognizing the contractor's problems, and assisting him with them in all practicable ways. He may also, in the normal course of conversation with the contractor, be able to reassure the contractor that excessively high performance will not be demanded. Nevertheless, he should indicate the contract clauses which provide him with powers to influence performance and the means needed to achieve satisfactory progress.

The majority of construction problems are not solved by techniques such as method study or operational research. Four practical cases of the value of control system methods in dealing with such construction problems are quoted in the Appendix. The first two cases (Appendix Examples 5 and 6) refer to the safety of permanent works and the last two (Examples 7 and 8) to the engineer's participation in overcoming construction difficulties. The cases illustrate some aspects of the quality of implementation needed to fulfil the control system.

Control system viability

Engineers may have reservations about adopting a control system on the grounds that it might increase their staff inputs and costs. They may also think that interventions in a contractor's operations attributable to a control system may increase his costs. These, however, are not the ultimate financial issue: that issue is whether or not the system is competent in minimizing the costs to the promoter of construction and postponement of project returns.

The treatment of construction problems by the methods of Section IV of the specimen type of system are demonstrated in Appendix Examples 1–4, 7 and 8. Though the actual savings in the costs of construction and postponement of returns cannot be calculated with any accuracy as the results of not using the methods can only be assessed and not seen, the savings are substantial. In one case — that of Example 8 — the savings (excluding savings in direct construction costs) would be £4 million if the measures taken averted four months of further delay. The cost-controlling propensities of other Sections of the specimen system may be assessed by inspection. The conclusion may be that the use of such a system is beneficial and virtually always results in substantial savings in costs to the promoter, often large even in relation to total project costs. If it is, any increases in the cost of the engineer's staff input and unjustified interventions in the contractor's operations are secondary and the promoter may be expected to accept them.

However, these staff and intervention cost increases are not likely to arise. The engineer's staff inputs required by all

Sections of the specimen type of system other than Section IV differ little from those needed by other methods of supervision. The inputs required by Section IV are to be compared with the inputs required when unjustified alterations and construction problem costs and delays have not been substantially cut by the methods set out there. It may also be seen that the level of staff required at any time to deal with any problem is not likely to exceed the level needed to do so less productively as the Section IV methods are not staff-intensive.

As to unjustified interventions in a contractor's operations, the inhibitions to unnecessary work are expressed in §§25,26,28,30,32–35,37,38,46,51–54,70,71,73,75,76 and 78 of the specimen system. There is also an emphasis on considering costs and benefits of any contemplated action to both the promoter and the contractor, which provides an atmosphere in which unjustified intervention does not thrive.

Introduction of control system

In considering any control system differing from his own, the engineer will evidently regard its first use as a trial. He will, however, expect initial difficulties. Though the type of system described here can be applied to minor works it is more easily introduced on works priced at over about £5 million. The senior staff concerned will then in the normal course be more experienced and the trial have both the scope and time to survive the first year's disappointments.

The initial head office and site staff's input may be planned on the following basis.

Total man-months with system (including inputs for occasional economy evaluation, method study and operational research) = Total man-months without system.

Some of the input for economy evaluation, method study and operational research may have to be obtained from external sources in the introductory phase. This may not be very efficient if advisors are not experienced in construction problems.

The provision of evaluation, method study and operational research services is different if a system of the specimen type is adopted generally. The engineer can then recruit or train so that a small proportion of his staff is skilled in one or more of these methods, not as specialists but as an added skill. They may work in the head office or on site as engineers or technicians, but generally be available to assist in normal economy evaluation, method study or operational research wherever the need arises. The special and rare case requiring more advanced evaluation, study or research is a matter for specialized advice.

6. Projects and engineers

Introduction

Projects and consequent needs for civil engineering may be public, private or jointly public and private. Public projects may be in line with sound government policy, and justified by economic evaluation or by national needs which are not directly economic, such as the arts and defence. On the other hand, they may not be in line with government policy, government policy may not be sound, or they may not be justified by economic evaluation or national non-economic need. This may be due to political circumstances, inadequate communication of policy, sectional interests leading to decisions of immediate convenience or other factors not difficult to comprehend. An engineer may have personal reasons for avoiding a certain type of project, but engineers taking part in feasibility studies will rarely, as engineers, be in a position to judge government policy or the economic and social worth of a project. With rare exceptions, they will only be able to assist in providing politicians and administrators with economic, operational and engineering advice on the project. Engineers concerned only with detailed engineering and construction of works forming part of a project will be less able to judge the project's ultimate merits. Evidence of sectional interest or of undesirable side-effects of a project is not sufficient cause for an engineer to disagree with a decision as to a project's justification; for instance, pollution might be preferable to starvation, economic stagnation or civil disturbance unknown to the engineer. The provision of engineering and, possibly, operating services in the evaluation of a project and its implementation will, however, be a significant contribution.

Public project identification and evaluation

Public projects are one among a number of measures the government authorizes to fulfil its economic policy, the formulation of which is assisted by some form of regular survey of the national economy and interim reviews or partial reviews of the latest survey available. The survey managers will know the government's general policies and may suggest or assume policies in areas not covered by the general policies, as necessary to provide a basis for the survey team's work. Among the survey team's conclusions will be recommendations including an allocation of public investment to various sectors of the economy — agriculture, industry, education, defence, health, transport, power, water supply and so on — and the recommendations will be backed by data, statistics, and by the survey team's judgements, forecasts and policy formation, interesting to, but more or less unexplored by, the engineer.

When the national economic survey has had government approval, it may be followed by periodic surveys of each sector aimed at recommending or identifying measures, including projects, to achieve the best balance between service standard and cost, and observing the recommendations, judgements and forecasts of the national economic survey. A sector survey may consist of

(*a*)   a general review of the public and private areas of the sector including the existing organization, powers and functions of the government department and any agencies responsible for the sector; their major assets, operations and performance; their finances; the costs of providing services; past and present demand for services; and existing development programmes

(*b*)   forecasts of demand for services in the sector

(*c*)   recommendations for immediately evident improvements in legislation, organization, operations, finances, facilities and equipment

(*d*)   identification of other improvements in those areas requiring further study

(*e*)   approximate cost estimates for projects recommended or identified in (*c*) and (*d*) and a recommended order of priority

(*f*)   a tentative revised development programme covering a selected number of years

59

Recommendations will be based on economic costs and benefits, the national economic survey, and judgement of standards of the services needed; and, where these criteria cannot be applied or where other factors, such as mobility of personnel, are concerned, on judgement.

If the government's knowledge of a particular sector is sparse and provides only a narrow base for planning development, an initial detailed sector survey may be undertaken to serve as the first of the periodic sector surveys. Data and statistics will be scarce and organization in the sector deficient, and the survey team will have to spend considerable time in collecting the former and establishing basic sector organization. The detailed work involved in this and in forecasting demand within the sector will be much greater than that needed for normal periodic survey and may require over ten times the staff input. One of the functions of the regular sector survey may be to recommend full-scale review of the last detailed survey as needed.

After reconciling the national economic survey and sector surveys, the government may approve feasibility studies of individual recommended projects. These will be carried out by the government or an appropriate government agency, possibly with the assistance of a firm of consultants. A feasibility study should include an examination of any existing organization, facilities and operations connected with the project; a forecast of demand for the project; alternative schemes for satisfying the demand; comparison of the alternative schemes on the basis of their economic costs and benefits; selection of any recommended scheme (i.e. the project); recommendations for managerial improvements; financial forecasts for operating the project; and outline engineering and operating details of the project, including drawings and cost estimates. The government and any government agency concerned will review the feasibility study and decide what action it is necessary to take.

A public project is an outcome of government policy and some form of national survey, sector survey and feasibility study. None of these is static: the findings of a sector survey may alter government policy or conclusions of a national survey; and, in the extreme, the findings of a feasibility study, such as estimates of cost, technological developments or opportunities for stimulating growth, may cause review and modification of sector and national conclusions and even government policy. Unforeseen political or social conditions, real or assumed urgency, or purely sectional interest may also affect the process of project evaluation.

Engineering can be a powerful generator of ill-considered projects. Large construction departments may select possible projects which have an appearance of usefulness, and prepare outline schemes on the grounds that, if the projects they represented were ever needed, this initial work would reduce the time required to carry them out. It is not a great step from this to conducting a more detailed study of the operational and engineering aspects of the schemes on the same grounds, with superficially convincing reports describing the schemes and presenting operating and engineering justifications, suitable preliminary drawings, outline specifications, and some estimate of the demand they would meet. Some schemes may be abandoned for lack of support, but others will continue to flourish. Before long, several of the schemes will be projects widely accepted as answering an obvious need, with ready-made detailed engineering, and without the need for economic feasibility study and consequent delay. The programming of national and sector surveys and major operations needed to complete projects, including feasibility studies, may inhibit the generation of unstudied major projects. Exceptions to satisfactory progress in carrying out the programme would have to be foreseen at the earliest date practicable and reviewed at an appropriate government level.

Broadly, the aims of a feasibility study should be to define a project (e.g. the development of a particular port or power station) which would meet demand, maximize the internal rate of return on investment and achieve a minimum rate of return fixed by the government or government agency (usually representing the opportunity cost of capital); and, where project assets are to be vested in a quasi-autonomous government agency (e.g. a port authority or electricity authority), to recommend charges necessary to achieve the degree of financial viability of the project (and, possibly, the agency) required by the government.

A feasibility study for the expansion of a port administered by a quasi-autonomous port authority could include

(*a*) a review of the port's existing operations, facilities and equipment (operations being taken as meaning organization, policy and general management, and working methods)

(*b*) a traffic forecast, based on the latest national economic survey and sector survey and information obtained from the departments responsible for updating them, the promoter, government departments and agencies, port users, unions, financial and industrial associations, and others

(*c*) engineering, operational and economic feasibility studies, including

(*i*) the preparation of alternative schemes for expansion to accommodate the traffic

(*ii*) a comparison of the alternative schemes on the basis of economic costs and benefits (i.e. costs and benefits to the national economy, not to the port authority)

(*iii*) a selection of the recommended scheme on the basis of the economic comparison and other effects on the public interest (e.g. pollution, effects on personnel)

(*iv*) an economic evaluation of the selected scheme

(*d*) site investigation including

(*i*) climatic conditions

(*ii*) sea and other hydraulic conditions (e.g. waves, water courses, currents, sedimentation)

(*iii*) ground conditions

(*iv*) other factors affecting construction and the finished works (e.g. availability of labour and materials, utilities, corrosion)

to enable alternative schemes to be prepared, the

selected scheme to be defined, and approximate cost estimates to be made

(*e*)   project details, including

> (*i*)   project definition and capital cost estimates
> (*ii*)   description of the project; including facilities, equipment on shore, floating equipment, land acquisition, operations (including accounting) consultant's services, staff training and consulting engineer's services
> (*iii*)   bases of cost estimates
> (*iv*)   technical details of facilities
> (*v*)   project programme and financing
> (*vi*)   proposed methods of procurement

(*f*)   a study of the port authority's finances, including

> (*i*)   a review of past operating results and balance sheets
> (*ii*)   a history of major events and policies affecting the authority's finances
> (*iii*)   estimates of cost-based charges for services to achieve financial viability
> (*iv*)   forecasts of income accounts, cash flows and balance sheets for several years
> (*v*)   financing of the project
> (*vi*)   forecasts of the financial rate of return on the authority's assets for a selected number of years
> (*vii*)   a review of the authority's insurance coverage
> (*viii*)   recommendations for financial policy and management

(*g*)   recommendations on port operations as defined in (*a*)
(*h*)   a summary of recommendations
(*i*)   outline engineering drawings and specifications for civil engineering facilities and outline specifications for equipment

Private project identification and evaluation
Private projects are also in general similarly based on

national or multi-national economic surveys, public sector surveys, where appropriate, and feasibility studies. They will, however, rest heavily on the firm's own market forecasts. The firm's studies will not aim at identifying projects needed to assist in achieving national economic objectives, but towards realizing opportunities for the firm. The feasibility study forecasts of the firm's share of the market will be fashioned in an attempt to optimize and quantify it by means of pricing policy, geographic location, assessment of political conditions and so on. Their evaluation will be based on commercial costs and benefits (i.e. to the firm, not to the national economy). This does not imply that private projects are less productive of public benefit.

Appraisal

A government department, government agency, firm or prospective lender will usually examine all aspects of a feasibility study coming from an external source, and prepare conditions they would require if they are to participate in the project. A government department may accept a project justification submitted by a government agency but assure itself of the project's consistency with the government's economic policy, the ability of the agency to finance the project, and the application of financial policies which the government considers sound to the project's operations. A firm may wish to review its own financial forecasts, confirm the efficiency of projected operating methods, and stipulate negotiations it must undertake with the government before finally considering the project. A lending agency may wish to prepare conditions for procurement, repayment of the loan and other conditions to be included in a loan agreement. These and similar questions are for final appraisal.

Appraisal may be substituted for a feasibility study when sufficient economic, operating, financial and engineering knowledge has been gathered and analysed to rule out significant danger of seriously misconceived decisions. It may also, at some risk, be substituted for feasibility study where there is a real or imagined need for speed. The appraisal will be similar to a feasibility study but less detailed in its treatment and not so concerned with maximizing as with attaining an adequate rate of return on investment. The elapse of time for an appraisal will be about one fifth of that for feasibility study.

Execution of a project

A project may consist of land acquisition; engineering work of any type; buildings; the supply of other assets; the establishment of, or improvements in, organization, management, working methods and manning; commissioning; and measures necessary for financing.

The civil engineering consultants' or department's participation will include the detailed engineering of civil engineering works, some buildings, and some mechanical, electrical and other engineering equipment supply and installation. Detailed engineering will include site investigation and survey for the civil engineering works and the buildings, and the preparation of contract documents for all the work. The civil engineering element will be completed by procurement and construction to a programme co-ordinated with programmes for other project elements. It may save time to telescope a feasibility study and detailed engineering. If the economic evaluation clearly indicates the selection of a particular scheme, the promoter may permit detailed site investigation and design to continue concurrently with work needed to complete the feasibility study. This latter will include preparation of project details, completion of the feasibility study report including drawings and reproduction, which occupy the month or two after the economic evaluation. The greater the overlap the greater is the risk of abortive work on detailed engineering, and the promoter's decision will imply a careful projection of the results of the feasibility study, appraisal and any other factors which may arise before making a final decision on the project.

Public sector programmes

National and sector surveys and feasibility studies will be major undertakings, interdependent and subject to considerable discussion before approval. It would be too much to expect the economic study and decision process to be so well-timed

and co-ordinated as to achieve a wholly satisfactory programme. The realization of sector programmes is, however,
also affected by time spent and respent due to administrative
negotiations, reconciliation with sectional interests, land
acquisition, financing arrangements, enabling legislation,
effects of changes in government policy, effects of technological development, construction delays, and effects of cost
increases, among other factors.

Departments and agencies responsible for detailed sector
programmes may counter unnecessary delays by producing
major project programmes on which all items which will
occupy significant times are shown and programmed as
clearly and simply as is practicable, so that those concerned
will be able to identify and carry out operations for which they
are responsible. The mere entry of the items such as administrative negotiations or land acquisition is marvellously clari-
fying to the mind and the knowledge that their progress will be
reviewed stresses needs for action. There are arguments for
excluding programmed contingency time as it amounts to time
allowed for no particular reason and is an invitation to delay.

Demands for changes in a project during feasibility study,
appraisal, detailed engineering, or construction for reasons
such as government policy changes, technological development
or construction delay assume the urgency and power of the
voices that make them. Some demands will be justified and
answerable only by changes, and some imperative. Others may
be withdrawn or rejected if the effects on programmes are
indicated clearly; a not inconsiderable service.

A sector programme may contain a list of projects of lower
priority, not recommended in the sector survey report for
implementation or immediate study, but considered to be worth
consideration in the future. A tentative order of priority for
these should be indicated so that a reserve list of projects is
available for further consideration if a sector programme
project is rejected, abandoned or delayed, or the programme is
expanded.

Engineering in preconstruction studies
The engineering contribution to any national economic

survey will be peripheral. A glance at the functions of a sector survey, however, will indicate that engineering participation is appreciable, particularly if the engineer is experienced in operations. The engineering participation in the type of feasibility study previously outlined would be

(*a*) a major part of the existing facilities and equipment review, and a substantial part of the operations review
(*b*) a relatively small part, such as discussion on the breakdown of traffic forecasts to correspond with different types of facilities, and assistance when general knowledge of the sector is useful
(*c*) the preparation of alternative schemes for expansion and assistance in the estimation of commercial (that is, financial, as distinct from economic) costs and benefits
(*d*) all site investigations
(*e*) the preparation of all physical details
(*f*) a small part, mainly supplying information required by the financial analyst
(*g*) a substantial part in preparing recommendations on operations
(*h*) the preparation of all engineering recommendations, a substantial part in preparing operations (excluding financial) recommendations and general assistance in preparing other recommendations
(*i*) all drawings and specifications

Engineers and project justification

Engineers are sometimes criticized for participating in public projects which are said to be unjustified or positively evil. This raises the general question of participation or refusal to participate. The engineer will seldom be in a position to pass judgement on a public project. Whatever economic and social studies have been undertaken, the government has the right to take its own confidential view of demand, costs, benefits and the opportunity of cost of capital; it may also privily consider that overriding benefits such as relieving ill effects of rapid development on its people, help in preserving national culture or service to the nation's religion justify the project. It may also have other cultural, strategic, social or political ends in mind which are unknown to the engineer. Such considerations leave the engineer with little basis for making judgements. If economic justification seems doubtful, he may advise the government of it, but he will rarely have any valid objection to the government's decision.

Limitations of these kinds affect the powers of economic study as an aid in making decisions both in the public and private sectors. Both governments and private sector firms, however, consider economic study worthwhile and arguments for and against present methodologies are of philosophic proportions, to which the engineer may consider himself fortunate in not aspiring. It remains, however, that the most important decisions with regard to a project are made before detailed engineering design and construction are required. Design and construction engineers therefore suddenly enter a project when major conclusions as to justification have been reached, then spend several years on its engineering, knowing little of the basis for the conclusions. In these conditions the promoter and engineer view the engineering in very different lights, the former with the aims and performance of the project as an economic entity throughout its life; and the latter tending to regard engineering as an object in itself.

There is no reason why it should not be common for engineers normally employed in design and construction to take part in economic studies and therefore in project decision-making. Much of their training and experience is relevant to the engineering, operational and financial cost and benefit evaluation elements of economic study, and many engineers could, by further training and experience, list economic study among their specializations as conveniently as, for instance, hydraulics, contract administration or some specialized type of design. It would open doors for practising engineers at all levels to policy and general management and provide the latter with the benefits of engineering ways of thinking.

Appendix: examples

The following examples are based on actual events. They have been edited to suit present purposes. They are also shorn of all but essential detail.

Example 1

A reinforced concrete piled wharf is under construction in sandy clay overlying rock. Piles subject to tension are being anchored by steel bars grouted into holes drilled in the rock, and about ten per cent of the piles are being placed in shallow holes bored into the rock to give pin-jointed restraint and end-bearing where the sandy clay overburden is thin. One fifth of the wharf piling has been placed or driven, working end over end, when hard rock is encountered and it becomes evident that neither the drilling nor boring equipment can penetrate it efficiently. The hard rock exists for 180 m of the 900 m of wharf still to be piled.

The engineer and contractor agree that there are three options.

(a) Option I. Continue with the present equipment until adequate equipment arrives, then complete the remainder of the piling using the new equipment.

(b) Option II. Complete the whole of the piling with the present equipment, drilling and boring shallower holes where the rock is hard.

(c) Option III. Continue with the present equipment until adequate equipment arrives. Use the heavier equipment to install the piling in the hard rock area, then return it to its owner and complete the remainder of the piling using the existing equipment.

The expected completion dates for Options II and III differ. The completion dates for the berths and associated shore facilities stipulated in the contract and expected of Options II and III are as follows.

69

	Contract	Option II	Option III
First two berths	1 Sept. 1976	27 Oct. 1976	1 Sept. 1976
Remaining berths	1 June 1977	26 July 1977	1 June 1977

The cost of Option III would be much less than that of Option I and its expected completion dates are satisfactory. Option I is therefore considered no further. The engineer discusses the late completion dates attending Option II with the promoter who gives him the estimated returns from the project. The promoter confirms that the delay in completion of the first two berths would cause loss in returns but says there would be no loss due to the delay in completing the remaining berths as the demand for additional berths would not have increased sufficiently by then to justify the costs of operating them. The estimated returns from the project (before interest and depreciation) assuming Options II and III are shown in Table 1. The date of the choice of option is 1 December, 1973 and the difference of £0.70 million is due to the difference in completion dates of the first two berths. No difference in returns in expected due to differing completion dates of the remaining berths.

The engineer considers that the contractor will be liable for additional costs and delays since adequate information on the hard

Table 1. Estimated returns from operating the project (£ million: 1973 prices)

	End of year	Option III (i.e. no delay)	Option II (i.e. eight weeks' delay)	Difference
Choice of Option (1 Dec. 1973)	0	0	0	—
	1	0	0	—
	2	0	0	—
	3	1.0	0.3	+ 0.7
Limited by	4	2.8	2.8	—
demand for	5	3.7	3.7	—
berths	6	4.9	4.9	—
	7	6.2	6.2	—
Approaching	8	6.9	6.9	—
full	9	6.7	6.7	—
utilization				

Table 2. Costs and benefits of Option III to promoter if liable

Costs	Benefits
The cost of dismantling existing drilling equipment and erecting the heavier equipment.	Direct construction cost savings due to reductions in delay to works other than piling.
The cost of dismantling the heavier equipment and re-erecting the existing equipment.	Earlier returns from the project due to eight weeks earlier completion.
The extra cost of piling with the heavier equipment.	

Table 3. Costs and benefits of Option III to promoter if liable (£ thousand: 1973 prices)

End of year	Costs	Benefits
0	20.0	2.0
1	20.0	3.0
2	—	3.0
3	—	702.0
4	—	—

rock was made available to him at the time of tendering. However, he continues with the analysis to investigate the effects of being wrong[1]. The costs and benefits to the promoter of Option III as compared with Option II should he prove liable would be as shown in Table 2.

The costs and benefits, estimated at constant 1973 prices and starting from the date when the option to be implemented is chosen, are shown in Table 3. The cost of dismantling and erecting equipment

---

[1]In practice the engineer would go no further as the benefit of increases in returns would greatly exceed the extra costs of Option III. The case is, however, developed here to consider method and the effect of different returns from a project.

is entered at year 0 and the second dismantling and erection cost at year 1. Half the extra cost of piling with the heavier equipment as compared with the cost of Option II is entered at year 0, and half at year 1. Estimated savings due to reduction in delay to works other than piling are entered at years 0 to 3; the savings are expected to approximate to a total of £10,000 on the basis that the contractor would have considerable flexibility in calling forward materials and equipment, dispensing with hired equipment and redistributing equipment, if Option II were chosen. The difference in returns from operating the project (Table 1) is shown at year 3.

The promoter expects a rate of return of 20% per annum from the project. Discounting at this rate, the present value of Option III would be approximately £376,200. This sum is a measure of the preference the promoter would have for the Option III scheme, if he were certain to be liable. This is evidently not so and the engineer makes his best judgement of the contractual liability of the promoter and the contractor and of what deviation from these liabilities will in fact take place in the final contract settlement. He estimates the probability of the contractor's being liable as 80% and therefore of the promoter's being liable as 20%. The saving of £700,000 in project returns is independent of liability.

The present value to the promoter of Option III would be

Present value of £700,000   = £405,090

0.20 of present value of other benefits and costs $= 0.20 \times -£28,900$ = −£5,780

Estimated present value to the promoter of adopting Option III   £399,310

The costs and benefits to the contractor of adopting Option III as compared with Option II would, if he were solely liable, be as in Table 4. The costs and benefits, estimated on the same basis as Table 3, are shown in Table 5, the differences at the years 0 and 1 representing contractor's profit; a nominal sum of £5,000 for liquidated damages avoided is entered at year 3.

Applying a rate of return of 20% to the contractor, the present value of Option III to him would be −£22,400. If the probability of liability is 80%, the present value to the contractor of Option III

Table 4. Costs and benefits of Option III to contractor if liable*

Costs	Benefits
The cost of dismantling existing drilling equipment and erecting the heavier equipment.	Direct construction cost savings due to reductions in delay to works other than piling.
The cost of dismantling the heavier equipment and reerecting the existing equipment.	Savings in liquidated damages not payable due to eight weeks earlier completion.
The extra cost of piling with the heavier equipment.	

*The benefits of earlier returns from the project due to earlier completion would not be available to the contractor.

Table 5. Costs and benefits of Option III to contractor if liable ($£$ thousand: 1973 prices)

End of year	Costs	Benefits
0	18.0	2.0
1	18.0	3.0
2	—	3.0
3	—	7.0
4	—	—

would be $0.80 \times -£22,400$, or approximately $-£17,900$; that is the present value of Option II would be $£17,900$.

As the estimated present value of Option III to the promoter is approximately $£400,000$ the engineer cannot accept a contractor's proposal to adopt Option II. A probable immediate result of negotiation would be that the contractor would agree that he saw no objection to Option III provided that he was paid at his valuation for adopting it. Option III would then be adopted and the contractor would state his claim.

Table 6. Costs and benefits of Option III to promoter if liable (£thousand: 1973 prices)

End of year	Costs	Benefits
0	20.0	2.0
1	20.0	3.0
2	—	3.0
3	—	52.0
4	—	—

Case where the engineer and contractor can compromise

Suppose that the traffic forecasts, the consequent demand for berths, and the project returns (Table 1) were such that the third year costs due to eight weeks delay were estimated as £50,000; that is the berths would not be in great demand. Table 3 would be replaced by Table 6.

If the probability of the promoter's being liable were 20%, the present value to him of adopting Option III would be

Present value of £50,000	= £28,935
0.20 × −£28,900	= −£5,780
Present value to promoter	£23,155

The costs and benefits to the contractor would remain as shown in Table 5 and the present value to him of Option II would be £17,900.

The engineer would not regard the contractor's proposal of Option II as unacceptable. He would, however, record his view on liability and delay. He might at the time be able to agree with the contractor measures to be taken to eliminate the delay. In any case he would take action under the contract to expedite progress, and, if necessary, would arrange for the promoter to be given the earliest practicable use of the wharves.

Example 2

Some time after work on site has started, the feasibility of changing the design of certain power station framing from steel to precast prestressed concrete is being considered, with the object of achieving savings in maintenance and replacement costs. The cost of the steel framing (Option I) is billed at £500,000 and it is estimated that the cost of the prestressed concrete framing (Option II) would be the same if built under the same conditions. A simplified comparison between the two options is given in Table 7.

The promoter has agreed that, if he took Option II, he would pay the engineer £5,000 for the additional design and contract documents. The estimated cost of abortive work already done by the contractor in ordering and detailing the steelwork is £7,000. The direct construction costs of delay in the framing construction and of dislocation of works dependent on the framing construction, together with the costs of measures the contractor would have to take to avoid delay in contract completion, are estimated at £40,000; this would be spread over approximately two and a half years of construction time. Estimated maintenance (including minor replacement) cost differences are also shown and the difference in residual values at 20 years is considered negligible. There are no other prospective benefits or costs of choosing Option II, such as differences in fire resistance. The resultant cash flow is also given.

At 15% per annum interest rate the extra cost to the promoter of changing the design to precast prestressed concrete, represented as a present value, would be £36,500 approximately and the design change would not be financially justified.

The promoter may have other reasons for preferring Option II. If they are quantifiable they can be included in the analysis, but, whether quantifiable or not, their benefits should be such as to outweigh a £36,500 present value advantage of Option I.

Example 3

An artificial channel is required to divert a stream around an industrial complex and its construction forms part of the contract for constructing the complex. The channel is trapezoidal in section and the design provides for an in situ concrete bed and precast concrete block sides.

During construction the contractor finds the precast block work slow for reasons which cannot be avoided, and, as the construction of major works will depend upon the channel, he experiments with laying in situ concrete at the steep slope of the sides. He finds this technically feasible and proposes the change in design to the engineer. The engineer estimates the cost to the contractor of precast concrete

75

Table. 7. Costs and benefits to promoter of framing design change (£ thousand: 1979 prices)

End of year	Contract documents	Abortive work	Delay	Maintenance (including minor replacement)	Residual value	Cash flow
0	5.0	—	5.0	—	—	10.0
1	—	7.0	15.0	—	—	22.0
2	—	—	15.0	—	—	15.0
3	—	—	5.0	—	—	5.0
4	—	—	—	—	—	—
5	—	—	—	—	—	—
6	—	—	—	-2.5	—	-2.5
7	—	—	—	-2.5	—	-2.5
8–19	—	—	—	-2.5 yearly	—	-2.5 yearly
20	—	—	—	-2.5	Negligible	-2.5

block construction as £120,000 and of the in situ concrete construction as £75,000. He also considers that the only difference between the contractor's proposal and the original design would be additional major repairs to the in situ concrete due to a lower resistance to heavy abrasion. He estimates these to be equivalent to £10,000 at nine years and £20,000 at 18 years after construction, both at prices prevailing at the time of construction. The promoter's expected rate of return is 8% per annum. The present value of the additional repairs is therefore approximately £10,000. There is evidently room for negotiation of an arrangement financially favourable to both the promoter and contractor.

Example 4

1,800,000 m³ (bulk measurement) of sand are required over a period of two years to form a sand-bank as a stable foundation and slope for piled wharves. The wharf contractor had considered dredging and transporting the sand himself but had eventually arranged with a dredging contractor, working with two dredgers some ten miles away on dredging and reclamation in sand, to load dumb barges provided by the wharf contractor, as an operation incidental to that of reclamation. The wharf contractor is towing between the dredger and the wharf site. The sand-bank has to be placed accurately, and the sand is being discharged and placed in position by three floating cranes with clam-shells. The operation works 20 hours per day and seven days per week, but progress is slow.

Analysis of the whole operation, that is, loading of sand from the dredgers into the barges, transportation to the wharf site, discharge into the sand-bank, the return journey to the dredgers, and the time waiting for reloading, is considered but not favoured as loading at the dredgers depends on conditions prevailing at the dredging and reclamation sites, which are complicated and difficult to express mathematically. The alternative of treating the sequence as a typical queuing problem is examined.

J. D. Mettam gives a convenient treatment in an article in *Dock and Harbour Authority,* April 1967, Issue No. 558, from which Fig. 1 has been taken. Applied to the present problem it is based on the assumption that the arrival of the barges can be considered as a random function following Poisson's law. Results depend also on the form of distribution of service times and the results of two assumptions are given in Fig. 1, one where $K = 1$ and the other where $K = \infty$.

In attempting to raise the productivity of the three-discharger

77

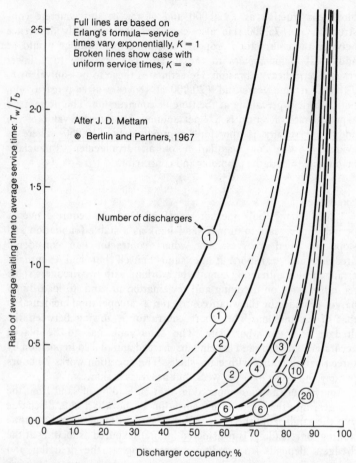

Fig. 1. Waiting time/service time and discharger occupancy relationships

installation the contractor has carried out a four-week trial under close supervision. The productivity of the three dischargers (approximately equal) has been improved and measured during the trial. When the operation is working well the rate of placing sand is about as programmed, discharger occupancy, about 80% and average waiting time per barge, 0.34 days. The barge arrivals are recorded and their behaviour approximates to a random function following Poisson's law. The basic data are as follows.

(a)   Rate of placing sand is 900,000 m³ per annum.

(b)   The barges are each of about 500 m³ capacity.

(c)   Poisson's law barge arrivals have been confirmed for the three-discharger case and are accepted for the four-discharger case.

(d)   In view of the uniformity of the barge capacities, Erlang distribution of service times with $K = \infty$ is accepted.

(e)   From observed performance, the average service time T_b needed to discharge one barge is 0.40 day (discharging time) + 0.10 day (time berthing alongside discharger, time from berthing to starting to discharge, and time from completing discharge to unberthing), i.e. $T_b = 0.5$ day.

(f)   Required rate of discharging barges = 900,000/500 = 1,800 per annum.

With three dischargers

$$\text{discharger occupancy} = \frac{1800 \times 0.50 \times 100}{3 \times 365} = 82\%$$

From Fig. 1, T_w/T_b, corresponding to 82% occupancy, three dischargers and Erlang $K = \infty$, would be 0.63, where T_w is the average waiting time per barge, i.e. $T_w/T_b = 0.63$. Therefore

$$T_w = 0.63 \times T_b = 0.63 \times 0.5 = 0.315 \text{ day}$$
total waiting time = $0.315 \times 1800 = 567$ days per annum

However, as found in operation, from Fig. 1 the waiting time would be sensitive to minor changes in circumstances. The waiting time would increase rapidly with small increases in service time.

With four dischargers

$$\text{discharger occupancy} = \frac{1800 \times 0.50 \times 100}{4 \times 365} = 62\%$$

Again from Fig. 1 it can be seen that $T_w/T_b = 0.11$. Therefore

$$T_w = 0.11 \times 0.50 = 0.06 \text{ day}$$
total waiting time = $0.06 \times 1800 = 108$ days per annum

The three-discharger option seems unacceptable. Minor reductions in the efficiency of discharging would cause either large increases in waiting time or reductions in the sand-placing rate. A reduction of 11% in discharging efficiency would cause virtually interminable waiting if the sand-placing rate were not reduced (Fig. 1), and equipment for transportation between the dredgers and the dischargers would be impossibly large.

The four-dredger option is attractive. It is not sensitive to reductions in discharging efficiency and waiting time would be small. Evidently there is no need to consider a five-discharger installation (which in any case would be impracticable on the ground of congestion of the site).

The choice between three and four dischargers is, however, not so clear. If the three-discharger option is accepted, the waiting time of the barges can be controlled by accepting a lower sand-placing rate from the dischargers, thus controlling the number of tugs and barges needed for transporting the sand. That is, the waiting time can be prevented from soaring up the steep slopes of the Fig. 1 graph. In this case the difference between the sand-placing rate and that needed to avoid delay would have to be provided by other means. The contractor finds that, as the timing of placing the marginal amount of sand is (within limits) not critical, he would be able to place it by hired hopper barge ahead of the dischargers in the lower levels of the sand-bank where accuracy of placing is not too stringent. The cost of this would be much less than the rental and running costs of an extra floating discharger and ancillary equipment (moorings etc.) and the option is therefore preferable to that of four dischargers.

The total cost of sand-placing can be minimized. The variable costs are costs of

(*a*)   tugs and barges serving the floating dischargers
(*b*)   dischargers and ancillary equipment
(*c*)   tugs and hopper barges placing directly into the sand-bank
(*d*)   congestion of the sand-placing
(*e*)   interdependence of sand-placing and other work
(*f*)   sand as received from the dredging contractor

On the basis of experience of the operation and Fig. 1, the contractor estimates that the total cost would be minimized by working the floating dischargers at 77% occupancy.

In this case the number of barges servicing the dischargers = $77 \times 3 \times 365/100 \times 50 = 1686$ per annum. From Fig. 1, at 70% occupancy

$$T_w/T_b = 0.44$$
$$T_w = 0.22 \times 0.50 = 0.22 \text{ day}$$
$$\text{total waiting time} = 0.22 \times 1686 = 371 \text{ days per annum}$$

The volume of sand placed by dischargers = $1686 \times 500 = 843{,}000$ m^3 per annum.

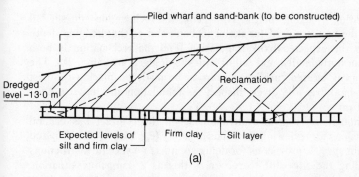

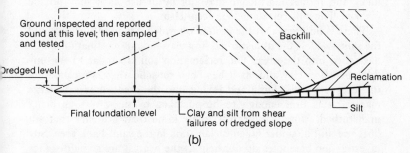

Fig. 2. Testing sand-bank foundation: (a) existing cross-section; (b) foundation clearance

The volume of sand placed by hopper barge = 900,000 −843,000 = 57,000 m³ per annum. The use of hopper barges can be varied to some extent as found desirable during construction.

Example 5

A reinforced concrete piled, suspended deck, deep water wharf is under construction on a site where a thin layer, about 1.50 m thick, of original silt has been left under the reclaimed area at approximately the future dredged level (Fig. 2a). The material in this layer is of very low shear strength and the wharf design includes dredging to the underside of it to allow a bank of sand to be deposited over the whole 1,000 m length wharf to avoid 'slip-circle' failure and form the slope to the designed wharf dredged level (13.00 m below low water). The face of the sand slope is to be protected by a layer of rubble and the wharf piling to be driven through the rubble and sand into undisturbed firm clay underlying the sand-bank.

81

During dredging for the sand-bank, the reclamation and silt fall into the area required for the sand-bank and as the dredging depth nears the expected bank foundation level the reclamation is both sliding horizontally, and falling into the dredged area (Fig. 2b). The bottom is cleared to allow a start to be made on placing the first sand-bank bay and divers inspect the foundation and report it clear and firm.

Though the control system in use on the contract has general provisions for reviewing questions of safety (e.g. SCS §§12,13,16) and certain specific provisions for doing so, it has no specific instructions enabling the site staff to recognize this as a dangerous situation. Experience is not a reliable guide as it may in the past have been lucky and formal knowledge may not be of use as it may not be invoked. The only certain help is scepticism.

There is no proof that the ground on which it is proposed to found the sand-bank is the undisturbed firm clay and not reclamation which has fallen into the area. The reclamation soil is similar to the un-disturbed firm clay and, as it has been consolidating as reclamation for ten years and sliding and falling into the dredged area in large masses, it is firm enough to be mistaken by the divers as being undisturbed. More significantly, there is no clear evidence that silt does not still lie under fallen reclamation in the sand-bank area. Site investigation boreholes do not help as the nearest are some distance away; and a distinction between undisturbed clay and reclamation soil in material brought up by the dredging is not conclusive.

The problem is not difficult. A split tube is driven into the ground at a selected number of spots in the cleared area. Over part of the area the tube drives fairly easily for a metre or so, after which it stiffens sharply. Though the sampling is primitive the distinction between the undisturbed clay and reclamation soil is evident when the tube is opened on shore. The method is used until the divers and site engineers develop their own simpler methods of recognizing the un-disturbed clay, after which the tube method is used only in cases of doubt.

Liability for the sampling and testing is part of a larger question of liability for the treatment of unforeseen foundation conditions, which the promoter accepts. The sampling and testing would have been called for by the engineer, however, if liability had been the contractor's (SCS§§68–81).

Example 6

In dredging to enlarge a canal, the canal bed at the foot of a slope

17.0 m high is being lowered slightly less than 1.5 m to provide a channel depth of 6.0 m, and the edge of the channel is to be 4.0 m from the toe of the slope. Stability conditions are therefore changed only slightly and the few boreholes put down in the area indicate that the slope will be stable. However, the engineer insists that, as a question of safety is concerned, provision for observations of the slope during dredging is included in the control system, though in general his staff think it pedantic. A line of stations is placed just above canal level in the slope before dredging starts. The line is in line with stations at each end and placed well beyond the area to be dredged. In view of the rapidity with which the slope might fail, the line is checked daily after the start of dredging.

Soon after the start of dredging, several of the stations located around the mid-point of the length of dredging completed begin to move slightly towards the channel. Dredging in the area is immediately stopped and dredgings from elsewhere are deposited at the foot of the slope. The movement of the slope ceases. Detailed investigation shows that the slope was barely stable before dredging, and a scheme is prepared for stabilizing it. The harbour channel is moved to 10.0 m from the toe of the slope. Liability under the contract is accepted by the promoter. Costs, however, are shared with local public authorities.

Example 7

Mass concrete breakwaters are under construction as part of the development of a port. The operation includes driving and extracting steel sheet piling, excavating, shuttering above water level, placing tie-bars and concreting. The breakwaters are being constructed end over end from the shore.

After teething problems the rate of construction picks up but it does not reach the programmed rate. The engineer suspects that the single crane at the end of each of two breakwaters cannot handle all the lifts required without causing delay. However

(*a*) a solution optimal to the contractor or the promoter may include changes in the permanent works, materials, equipment, the contractor's or engineer's staff or labour, or construction methods

(*b*) the solution may be affected by unavoidable physical conditions (e.g. weather, ground, obstructions) which may deteriorate or improve

(*c*) all operations carried out before and after the cranes affect the crane operation

(*d*) whatever his regard for the contractor, the engineer cannot assume that he will pay the same attention to delays in completion as the promoter, as liquidated damages would be much less than losses due to postponement of returns

The various possibilities have been examined and it has been agreed without prejudice that either an additional crane is required at each breakwater or operations requiring the cranes must be retimed, or both, and the expense of additional cranes must be avoided if retiming operations would suffice. The problem seems suitable for simple method study and the engineer considers its feasibility. He estimates the savings in direct construction costs of eliminating delay as about £10,000 per week of delay eliminated, and savings due to earlier completion and therefore returns from the project as about £20,000 per week of time saved. A simple method study carried out by site staff would cost about £250. The figures do not express the costs and benefits to the promoter of expending the £250: what savings would be achieved and costs incurred if the method study were not carried out are not known; what expenditure would be necessary additional to the £250 (e.g. in additional equipment) is not known; and the question of liability has not been considered. However the engineer, viewing the order of savings and costs, thinks the prospects of returns from spending £250 in method study justify the expenditure.

At this stage the contractor has been trying various methods to improve progress in the normal course of works management for several weeks, with some but insufficient success. He has naturally had in mind the prospect of doing so without incurring the costs of additional cranes, and alternatively of ascertaining whether providing the cranes would eliminate all delays. However the engineer considers that delay to date is reaching an extent which the contractor would be unable to recover, and that, therefore, unavoidable delay in completion will shortly be incurred by further inaction. On the other hand it would be unwarrantable and perhaps costly to the promoter to exert pressure on the contractor if there were no danger of delay in completion. He decides to carry out the method study. The cost is low and to some extent notional as the engineer's representative has time on his hands due to the delay, and he decides to carry out the study himself.

As a result of the study, the engineer's views are as follows.

(*a*) The crane on each breakwater cannot handle all the lifts required of it as the work is at present organized.

(*b*)   There is little scope for improving the cranes' productivity by re-scheduling the work.

(*c*)   It is virtually certain that the construction rate would be satisfactory if additional cranes were installed.

He presents these views to the contractor and quotes the cost to the employer of delay in completion. The required additional capacity is provided and there is no claim.

Method study as it is used here consists of preparing a flow process chart for existing operations affecting the crane, and attempting to build up an efficient breakwater construction process without over-utilizing the crane. No work measurement to establish standard times is undertaken.

Example 8

The engineer's representative on the construction of a barrage reviews progress nine months after the completion of initial plant and temporary works erection and, as more or less expected, finds the state of permanent works progress and of coffer-dam construction to be half of that programmed, and the rate of progress on each about half of that programmed. The rate of progress has not increased during the last two months. The interim certificates, after deducting advances, reflect this position.

There have been no delays in delivery of the equipment nor in the delivery and erection of fixed plant, no shortages of staff or labour, nor lack of particular skills. There have been no exceptional physical difficulties.

The contractor's agent's explanations for slow progress have been that physical conditions are unfavourable. He has quoted under-ground obstructions to driving coffer-dam piling and explained that the rate of progress will soon pick up. But the engineer's representative examining the bore-hole records of the original site investigation, has found the encountered incidence of obstructions less than that which should have been expected. No explanation is offered for delays in other works, other than a statement of the physical fact that the various operations making up a particular work have not yet picked up speed. No work, with the exception of desultory excavating in soft material, is progressing at more than half-speed.

The engineer's representative tells the contractor's agent that both the state of progress and the rate of progress are unsatisfactory and asks him for proposals for improvement. The answer is unsatisfactory. The engineer's representative reports to the engineer who passes on the substance of the report to the contractor and requests proposals. The contractor asks for a meeting with the engineer and this takes place, but after a month has passed no effective proposals for action have been received.

The engineer's view is as follows.

(*a*) The cost to the promoter of delay in completion, though complicated by seasonal needs for irrigation, may be regarded as £1.0 million per month of delay.

(*b*) To date there have been serious delays over and above unavoidable start-up delays, and current production rates are 50% low. There has been no physical reason for this.

(*c*) The contractor's site management is inadequate and the directors are not dealing with that problem. It is therefore useless to attempt to treat construction problems on the basis of SCS§§68–81 until the management has been improved.

(*d*) No further delay in taking action is permissible.

The engineer tells the contractor that he has the alternatives of either replacing his agent or sending a director to the site for two months, after which any further action necessary would be considered. The engineer and the contractor have worked together before and the engineer names the director, known to him as a highly competent agent. The contractor strongly opposes either action but offers no valid alternative and eventually undertakes to try the latter course.

The engineer examines his own performance. The engineer's representative has mentioned that a number of disrupting and apparently unjustified Variations have been and are being generated by the promoter and the engineer. They find under preparation an ominously large number of such Variations and of working drawings which contain changes that have not been scheduled as Variations. Most of these have not been included in the latest financial review and their effects on claims are not entered in the claims register. The control system process of justification (SCS§§43–54) has not been followed and the master copy of the contract details is not complete. It is obvious that the contract price and programme would be seriously affected if all the proposed Variations and working drawings were issued (SCS§§123–125). The engineer's representative prepares a revised financial review and programme, both of which alarm the promoter, and the engineer negotiates with the promoter a reduction in changes requested by him. He also orders reductions in changes contemplated or under preparation by his own office. The reductions are based on need for, and economy of, proposed changes. The engineer also fixes dates at three-monthly intervals when he and the engineer's representative will review action under the control system.

The contractor's agent retains his position and the director takes up an unobtrusive role. The rate of progress improves satisfactorily and the director leaves after three months, continuing as director-in-charge of the contract. The solution proves satisfactory.

References

For the purposes of construction control, study of References 3, 4 and 6 and of relevant parts of other References is recommended. General reading of other parts is useful.

1   Currie, R. M. *Work Study*. Revised by Dr J. E. Faraday. Pitman Publishing/Management Publications Ltd for the British Institute of Management.
2   Grant, E. L. and Ireson W. G. *Principles of engineering economy* New York: The Ronald Press Company.
3   Hancock, P. H. D. Contract Management and Control in *Civil Engineer's reference book* ed. L. S. Blake. London: Newnes-Butterworths.
4   Pouliquen, L. Y. *Risk analysis in project appraisal* World Bank Occasional Papers No. 11. London and Baltimore: The Johns Hopkins Press.
5   Sasieni, Yaspan and Friedman *Operations research: methods and problems*. New York and London: John Wiley and Sons.
6   *Civil engineering procedure*. London: Institution of Civil Engineers.
7   *Conditions of Contract and forms of tender, agreement and bond for use in connection with work of civil engineering construction*. ('ICE Conditions of Contract') Fifth edition, June 1973 (revised 1979). London: Institution of Civil Engineers.
8   *Engineering Economics*. London: Institution of Civil Engineers.